UNDERSTANDING
PSYCHOLOGY

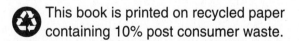
This book is printed on recycled paper containing 10% post consumer waste.

GLENCOE

Macmillan/McGraw-Hill

New York, New York   Columbus, Ohio   Mission Hills, California   Peoria, Illinois

TO THE TEACHER

Tests contains reproducible chapter tests for *Understanding Psychology.* Each test contains 45 objective question and 2 essay questions. Each chapter test has two versions, Form A and Form B.

Send all inquiries to:
Glencoe Division
McGraw-Hill
936 Eastwind Drive
Westerville, Ohio 43081

ISBN 0-02-823163-5

Printed in the United States of America.

1 2 3 4 5 6 7 8 9 BAW 99 98 97 96 95 94

Table of Contents

Chapter Tests

CHAPTER 1

Test

Form A

INTRODUCING PSYCHOLOGY

Directions: In the space at the left, write the letter of the choice that best completes the statement or answers the question. (2 points each)

_____ 1. The vast majority of psychologists study
   a. learning and memory processes
   b. very complex human processes
   c. commonplace behavior and feelings
   d. abnormal behavior

_____ 2. Mnemonic devices are
   a. electrical measures of brain activity
   b. ways of studying group interactions
   c. methods of rewarding desired behavior
   d. memory aids

_____ 3. The pursuit of knowledge for its own sake is called
   a. applied science   **c.** clinical psychology
   b. basic science   **d.** educational psychology

_____ 4. A complex explanation based on findings from many studies is a(n)
   a. basic science   **c.** theory
   b. applied science   **d.** mnemonic aid

_____ 5. The concept of "unconscious determinants of behavior" is associated with
   a. Freud   **c.** Wundt
   b. Watson   **d.** Pavlov

_____ 6. _____ psychology is association with psychotherapy.
   a. Clinical   **c.** Personnel
   b. Developmental   **d.** Social

_____ 7. Psychologists' goals include
   a. describing and explaining behavior
   b. predicting behavior
   c. controlling behavior
   d. all of the above

_____ 8. Which of the following is not associated with B. F. Skinner?
   a. *Walden Two*   **c.** free association
   b. reinforcement   **d.** behaviorism

_____ 9. Memory, problem solving, and intelligence are within the domain of _____ psychologists.
   a. clinical   **c.** educational
   b. school   **d.** counseling

_____ **10.** Experimental psychologists are primarily concerned with
   a. basic science   **c.** animal science
   b. applied science   **d.** all of the above

Directions: Place a + in the space at the left of each true statement. Place a 0 at the left of each false statement. (2 points each)

_____ **11.** William James established the first psychology laboratory in Leipzig.

_____ **12.** Psychological research focuses on broad questions.

_____ **13.** Mnemonic devices only help you learn strategies to learn.

_____ **14.** Galton based his studies on biographies.

_____ **15.** Freud's research tool was naturalistic observation.

_____ **16.** Hypotheses must be formulated so that they can be supported or not supported.

_____ **17.** Wundt is often referred to as the founder of psychology as a science.

_____ **18.** Skinner was the formulator of American behaviorism.

_____ **19.** Skinner developed the teaching machine.

_____ **20.** Social psychologists study groups.

Directions: In the space at the left, write the term or terms that best complete the statement. (2 points each)

_____ **21.** Psychologists, on the whole, study _____ behavior.

_____ **22.** Informal rules, or _____ , guide much of our social behavior.

_____ **23.** Understanding psychology can provide useful _____ into behavior.

_____ **24.** Memory aids, or _____ devices, help in rote learning.

_____ **25.** Systematic dispensing of rewards and punishments to guide an organism's responses is called _____ .

_____ **26.** Some thinkers popularized _____ , the idea that the mind and body are separate and distinct.

_____ **27.** _____ science involves the accomplishment of practical goals.

_____ **28.** Psychology as an independent science began more than _____ years old.

_____ **29.** According to Freud, _____ reveals the operation of unconscious processes.

_____ **30.** Many personality and intelligence tests derive from the work of _____ .

_____ **31.** The position of behaviorism was formulated by _____ .

_____ **32.** Skinner's technique of _____ , or controlled rewards, has had a major impact on modern education.

_____ **33.** Clinical psychology is an example of _____ science.

_____ **34.** _____ psychologists deal with topics related to teaching children and young adults.

_____ **35.** _____ psychologists are the basic scientists of the profession.

Directions: Match each person or term in the left column with the best association. Write the letter of the association in the space provided. (2 points each)

_____ **36.** Wundt

_____ **37.** Freud

_____ **38.** Galton

_____ **39.** Pavlov

_____ **40.** Watson

_____ **41.** Skinner

_____ **42.** clinical psychology

_____ **43.** Maslow

_____ **44.** hypothesis

_____ **45.** engineers

a. applied science

b. *Beyond Freedom and Dignity*

c. conditioned reflex

d. educated guess

e. founder of American Behaviorism

f. referred to as founder of modern psychology

g. humanistic psychology

h. individual differences

i. psychotherapy

j. discussed unconscious motivations

Directions: Answer the following questions in the space provided. (5 points each)

46. Discuss and illustrate the concepts of basic and applied science.

_____

_____

_____

_____

_____

_____

_____

_____

_____

_____

47. Discuss and give examples of the subspecializations found in contemporary psychology.

_____

_____

_____

_____

_____

_____

_____

_____

_____

_____

CHAPTER 1 Test

Form B

INTRODUCING PSYCHOLOGY

Directions: In the space at the left, write the letter of the choice that best completes the statement or answers the question. (2 points each)

_____ 1. Hypotheses
   a. are educated guesses
   b. have to be empirically tested
   c. have to be able to be supported or not supported
   d. are all of the above

_____ 2. Psychologists who use psychological principles to solve immediate problems are practicing
   a. basic science   **c.** socioeconomic psychology
   b. applied science   **d.** behaviorism

_____ 3. The subfield of industrial psychology generally includes
   a. basic psychologists
   b. applied psychologists
   c. both a and b
   d. neither a nor b

_____ 4. The first modern psychologist was
   a. Freud   **c.** Galton
   b. Wundt   **d.** Skinner

_____ 5. Which of the following is associated with psychotherapy?
   a. clinical psychology
   b. developmental psychology
   c. personnel psychology
   d. social psychology

_____ 6. The field of individual differences and intelligence testing is associated with
   a. Watson   **c.** Freud
   b. Pavlov   **d.** Galton

_____ 7. Psychologists' goals include
   a. describing and explaining behavior
   b. predicting behavior
   c. controlling behavior
   d. all of the above

_____ 8. About what percentage of all psychologists specialize in clinical psychology?
   a. 50 percent   **c.** 3 percent
   b. 10 percent   **d.** 75 percent

_____ 9. Galton devised the
   a. conditioned reflex   **c.** case record
   b. utopian community   **d.** personality test

_____ **10.** *Inquiries into Human Faculty and its Development* was written by
      a. Freud   **c.** Galton
      b. Skinner   **d.** Wundt

Directions: Place a + in the space at the left of each true statement. Place a 0 at the left of each false statement. (2 points each)

_____ **11.** Shaping is a systematic method of rewarding and punishing behavior.

_____ **12.** Free association is associated with Galton.

_____ **13.** Freud denied the importance of biology for behavior.

_____ **14.** Experimental psychologists do basic science.

_____ **15.** Basic science is the finding of immediate uses for knowledge.

_____ **16.** Most babies do best with high levels of stimulation.

_____ **17.** Wundt's main research method was introspection.

_____ **18.** Watson accepted the presence of instincts in humans.

_____ **19.** Clinical psychologists usually work in schools.

_____ **20.** The teaching machine is associated with educational psychology.

Directions: In the space at the left, write the term or terms that best complete the statement. (2 points each)

_____ **21.** Psychologists who stressed investigating observable behavior became known as _____ .

_____ **22.** Forensic psychology applies psychological principles to the _____ system.

_____ **23.** The Cultural Revolution led to a rebirth of psychology in _____ .

_____ **24.** A(n) _____ is an educated guess about the relationship between variables.

_____ **25.** _____ science is the pursuit of knowledge for its own sake.

_____ **26.** _____ psychologists believe that psychological events are the result of biological or chemical processes.

_____ **27.** _____ established the first psychology laboratory.

_____ 28. _____ published the idea that the earth revolved around the sun.

_____ 29. The concept of unconscious motivation was at the heart of the studies by _____ .

_____ 30. Wundt used a method of self-observation called _____ to collect information about the mind.

_____ 31. Goals of psychology include description, explanation, _____ , and control.

_____ 32. A person may be motivated by his or her _____ , or physiological, state.

_____ 33. A person may behave in a certain way because of his or her _____ , or mental state.

_____ 34. Specialists in clinical psychology are often referred to as _____ .

_____ 35. _____ psychologists such as Carl Rogers describe human nature as active and creative.

Directions: Match each person or term in the left column with the best association. Write the letter of the association in the space provided. (2 points each)

_____ 36. theory

_____ 37. forensic

_____ 38. dualism

_____ 39. free association

_____ 40. Walden II

_____ 41. industrial/organizational

_____ 42. James

_____ 43. Copernicus

_____ 44. Galileo

_____ 45. Descartes

a. explanation of findings

b. *Principles of Psychology*

c. theorized that earth is not center of universe

d. method pioneered by Freud

e. idea that mind and body are distinct

f. contended mind influenced body

g. field of psychology that studies workings of legal system

h. communities that followed behaviorist principles

i. field of psychology that studies the workplace

j. used telescope to confirm predictions

Directions: Answer the following questions. Use a separate sheet of paper if necessary. (5 points each)

46. Discuss at least two historical trends found in modern psychology.

_____

_____

_____

_____

_____

_____

_____

_____

_____

_____

47. Discuss the basic reasons for studying psychology.

_____

_____

_____

_____

_____

_____

_____

_____

_____

_____

_____

CHAPTER 2 Test

Form A

LEARNING: PRINCIPLES AND APPLICATIONS

Directions: In the space at the left, write the letter of the choice that best completes the statement or answers the question. (2 points each)

_____ 1. In classical conditioning, the best results occur when the conditioned stimulus is presented
   a. after the unconditioned stimulus
   b. at the same time as the unconditioned stimulus
   c. alone
   d. before the unconditioned stimulus

_____ 2. Watson demonstrated how _____ could be conditioned.
   a. discrimination learning
   b. salivation
   c. fear
   d. intimacy

_____ 3. A child saying "Daddy" only to his father is an example of
   a. extinction
   b. discrimination
   c. generalization
   d. an unconditioned response

_____ 4. A subject responding to a second stimulus similar to the original CS is an example of
   a. discrimination   **c.** generalization
   b. preconditioning   **d.** taste

_____ 5. Harlow demonstrated with animals the phenomenon of _____ .
   a. learned laziness
   b. operant conditioning
   c. learned helplessness
   d. learning to learn

✳ _____ 6. In classical conditioning, the unconditioned stimulus elicits
   a. an automatic response
   b. a learned response
   c. a conditioned stimulus
   d. salivation

_____ 7. In classical conditioning, the responses that are conditioned are
   a. voluntary
   b. involuntary
   c. operant
   d. imitative

_____ **8.** An unpleasant consequence that decreases the frequency of the response that produced it is called
   a. negative reinforcement
   b. punishment
   c. classical conditioning
   d. avoidance learning

_____ **9.** Individuals who believe that no matter what they do, their actions make no difference are exhibiting
   a. aversive control
   b. extinction
   c. learned helplessness
   d. response chains

_____ **10.** We expect life and death types of responses to be learned by
   a. modeling
   b. classical conditioning
   c. operant conditioning
   d. shaping

Directions: Place a + in the space at the left of each true statement. Place a 0 at the left of each false statement. (2 points each)

_____ **11.** Reinforcement can be defined as learning from the lack of consequences of behavior.

_____ **12.** Pavlov demonstrated that a neutral stimulus can elicit an unrelated response if it is presented before a stimulus that normally induces that response.

_____ **13.** Skinner is the psychologist most closely associated with operant conditioning.

_____ **14.** Smiles and approval are primary reinforcers.

_____ **15.** Disinhibition is a form of modeling often used in clinical work.

_____ **16.** Humans depend less on learning than other species.

_____ **17.** In Pavlov's experiment, food was the unconditioned stimulus.

_____ **18.** Responses are learned better when reinforced on fixed schedules.

_____ **19.** Practice is the key element that makes for smooth movement from response to response.

_____ **20.** Correct avoidance behavior is never learned by imitation.

Directions: In the space at the left, write the term or terms that best complete the statement. (2 points each)

_____ 21. _____ is a lasting change in behavior resulting from experience.

* _____ 22. At the start of Pavlov's experiment, salivation was the _____ response.

_____ 23. When an organism responds to a new stimulus that is similar to the original conditioned stimulus, it is called _____ .

_____ 24. The psychologist _____ demonstrated conditioning on a human infant.

* _____ 25. If you stop presenting the unconditioned stimulus, the conditioned response lessens in strength. This process is called _____ .

_____ 26. Skinner is the psychologist most closely associated with _____ conditioning.

* _____ 27. Rewarding consequences that follow a behavior are called positive _____ .

_____ 28. A total of _____ basic schedules of reinforcement have been studied.

_____ 29. On a(n) _____ schedule, reinforcement is available at predetermined times.

_____ 30. When signals are reinforcers in and of themselves, they are called _____ reinforcers.

_____ 31. In negative reinforcement, the removal of unpleasant consequences _____ the frequency of a behavior that preceded the removal.

_____ 32. When previously learned responses help in learning a new task, it is called _____ transfer.

_____ 33. In learning, chains of responses are put together into response _____ .

_____ 34. In CAI, students receive _____ reinforcement after each unit.

_____ 35. Getting points that can be cashed in for candy is an example of the _____ system of learning.

Directions: Match each person or term in the left column with the best association. Write the letter of the association in the space provided. (2 points each)

_____ 36. Pavlov

_____ 37. generalization

_____ 38. Little Albert

_____ 39. Skinner

_____ 40. Harlow

_____ 41. Seligman

_____ 42. modeling

_____ 43. teaching machine

_____ 44. fixed-ratio schedule

_____ 45. variable-ratio schedule

a. broadening of a response

b. classical conditioning

c. learned helplessness

d. learning to learn

e. observational learning

f. operant conditioning

g. pieceworker

h. programmed instruction

i. slot machine

j. Watson

Directions: Answer the following questions on a separate sheet of paper. (5 points each)

46. Develop a design to create fear of a rabbit in a young child. Also develop a plan to extinguish this fear.

47. Describe several factors that help or hinder the learning process.

CHAPTER 2 Test

Form B

LEARNING: PRINCIPLES AND APPLICATIONS

Directions: In the space at the left, write the letter of the choice that best completes the statement or answers the question. (2 points each)

_____ 1. Responding to a class of stimuli rather than a specific stimulus is called
    a. discrimination
    b. generalization
    c. operant conditioning
    d. classical conditioning

_____ 2. An animal that is reinforced for every fifth response is on a
    a. fixed-interval schedule
    b. fixed-ratio schedule
    c. variable-ratio schedule
    d. variable-interval schedule

_____ 3. A gambler at a slot machine operates on a _____ schedule of reinforcement.
    a. fixed ratio
    b. fixed interval
    c. variable interval
    d. variable ratio

_____ 4. Objects that satisfy or reduce a basic, natural need are called
    a. feedback
    b. secondary reinforcers
    c. aversive controls
    d. primary reinforcers

✳ _____ 5. If we wished to train a dog to fetch a paper we would probably use
    a. classical conditioning
    b. modeling
    c. shaping
    d. PSI

_____ 6. A relatively permanent change in behavior that results from experience is _____ .
    a. feedback
    b. learning
    c. imitation
    d. extinction

_____ 7. On a _____ schedule, the time of which reinforcement becomes available changes.
    a. fixed-interval
    b. variable-interval
    c. variable-ratio
    d. fixed-ratio

_____ 8. Harlow's experiments showed that animals
    a. could do nothing to avoid being shocked
    b. salivated when a tone was presented
    c. can learn to use strategies to solve problems
    d. only learn through escape conditioning

_____ 9. Aversive stimuli can affect behavior by acting as negative reinforcers or as
    a. punishers   c. feedback
    b. transfer   d. positive reinforcers

_____ 10. The type of conditioning system used in group situations with problem children is called
    a. CAI
    b. token economy
    c. modeling
    d. classical conditioning

Directions: Place a + in the space at the left of each true statement. Place a 0 at the left of each false statement. (2 points each)

_____ 11. Operant conditioning involves learning from the consequences of behavior.

_____ 12. Intermittent reinforcement leads to less stable behavior than continuous reinforcement.

_____ 13. A variable-ratio schedule leads to a steady high rate of responding.

_____ 14. Seligman believes that learned helplessness is a major cause of depression.

_____ 15. Learned laziness is the result of rewards coming without effort.

_____ 16. Learning is best described as a temporary change in behavior.

_____ 17. Extinction of a response is always permanent.

_____ 18. In punishment, an unpleasant consequence decreases the frequency of the behavior that produced it.

_____ 19. Pavlov's major experiment dealt with taste aversions.

_____ 20. Punishment and negative reinforcement are identical.

Directions: In the space at the left, write the term or terms that best complete the statement. (2 points each)

* _____ **21.** The principles of _____ conditioning were discovered by Pavlov.

* _____ **22.** A(n) _____ response is learned in classical conditioning.

_____ **23.** Generalization occurs when an animal responds to a second _____ similar to the original CS.

_____ **24.** The ability to respond differently to distinct stimuli is called _____ .

_____ **25.** Becoming ill after eating a certain food may result in a taste _____ .

_____ **26.** Behavior that is reinforced every time it occurs is based on a _____ schedule.

_____ **27.** If a schedule is based on the number of correct responses an organism makes between reinforcements, it is a(n) _____ schedule.

_____ **28.** A stimulus or event that affects the likelihood that a behavior will be _____ is called a reinforcer.

_____ **29.** In _____ reinforcement, an unpleasant stimulus is removed or not applied at all.

* _____ **30.** In _____ reinforcement, the removal of unpleasant consequences increases the frequency of a behavior.

_____ **31.** Seligman demonstrated the concept of learned _____ .

_____ **32.** In _____ conditioning, a person's behavior causes an unpleasant event to stop.

_____ **33.** Getting points that can be cashed in for candy is an example of the _____ system of learning.

_____ **34.** _____ is the effects of past learning on the ability to learn new tasks.

_____ **35.** Disinhibition is an example of learning from _____ .

Directions: Match each term in the left column with the best association. Write the letter of the association in the space provided. (2 points each)

✳ _____ **36.** extinction

_____ **37.** discrimination

_____ **38.** reinforcement

_____ **39.** escape conditioning

✳ _____ **40.** operant conditioning

✳ _____ **41.** classical conditioning

_____ **42.** conditioned stimulus

✳ _____ **43.** unconditioned stimulus

✳ _____ **44.** unconditioned response

_____ **45.** primary reinforcer

a. an event that leads to a certain, predictable response

✳ **b.** a neutral event that, after training, leads to a response

c. satisfies or reduces a basic need

✳ **d.** learning procedure in which stimulus that normally brings about a response is repeatedly preceded by a neutral stimulus

e. training of an organism to remove an unpleasant stimulus

✳ **f.** a reaction that occurs naturally and automatically in response to a UCS

✳ **g.** learning from the consequences of behavior

h. a stimulus or event that affects the likelihood that a behavior will be repeated

✳ **i.** gradual disappearance of a conditioned response

j. ability to respond differently to different stimuli

Directions: Answer the following questions on a separate sheet of paper. (5 points each)

46. Discuss the differences between classical and operant conditioning.

47. How would you get a pigeon to peck at a red circle to get food? Be specific.

Test Form A

MEMORY AND THOUGHT

Directions: In the space at the left, write the letter of the choice that best completes the statement or answers the question. (2 points each)

_____ 1. Chunking is associated with
    a. sensory storage   **c.** short-term memory
    b. long-term memory   **d.** recognition

_____ 2. Photographic memory is also called
    a. eidetic memory   **c.** mnemonic memory
    b. confabulation   **d.** recall

_____ 3. Interference refers to
    a. intentionally blocking an unpleasant memory
    b. fading of memories over time
    c. blocking of a memory by previous or subsequent memories
    d. inability to store short-term memories

_____ 4. Which of the following applies to the ability to identify the name of your first-grade teacher in a newspaper article?
    a. confabulation   **c.** recognition
    b. selective attention   **d.** recall

_____ 5. While playing tennis a scientist realizes the solution to a problem. This is called
    a. directed thinking   **c.** problem solving
    b. symbolic thinking   **d.** nondirected thinking

_____ 6. Which of the following is a combination of the other three?
    a. recombination   **c.** flexibility
    b. creativity   **d.** original use of information

_____ 7. While entertaining a group of friends in the living room, you hear your infant sister crying in the bedroom. This is an example of
    a. feature extraction   **c.** recall
    b. sensory storage   **d.** selective attention

_____ 8. Short-term memories
    a. last without rehearsal
    b. last about one minute
    c. last about one-half second
    d. have a limited capacity

_____ 9. Psychologist George Miller theorized that short-term memory is limited to about
    a. 7 items   **c.** 1 hour
    b. 10 words   **d.** 14 numbers

_____ **10.** The "aha" experience, or suddenly realizing the solution to a problem, is called
  a. functional fixedness
  b. a concept
  c. insight
  d. symbolic thinking

Directions: Place a + in the space at the left of each true statement. Place a 0 at the left of each false statement. (2 points each)

_____ **11.** Selective attention blocks out all stimuli except the one you attend to.

_____ **12.** Short-term memory lasts for less than 20 seconds without rehearsal.

_____ **13.** According to some theories, to recall a particular event, you should try to recreate the mood you were in when it happened.

_____ **14.** Short-term memory can store about 12 unrelated items.

_____ **15.** A multiple-choice question retrieves information through recall.

_____ **16.** Input is the information one receives from his or her senses.

_____ **17.** Basic needs are the top priority in deciding the importance of input.

_____ **18.** Recall is not affected by knowledge or expectations.

_____ **19.** Confabulation can include wrong or fictional information.

_____ **20.** Freud's explanation for forgetting is repression.

Directions: In the space at the left, write the term or terms that best complete the statement. (2 points each)

_____ **21.** All cognitive activity is referred to as _____ processing.

_____ **22.** Picking out a face in a crowd is an example of _____ .

_____ **23.** _____ means being able to make fine distinctions between similar inputs.

_____ **24.** _____ holds information for a fraction of a second.

_____ **25.** Items in your mind at any given moment are in _____ memory.

_____ **26.** _____ memory stores information for future use.

_____ **27.** Recite and Review are the last two steps in the _____ method.

_____ 28. The ability to _____ suggests that more is stored in memory than is commonly thought.

_____ 29. _____ is the active reconstruction of information.

_____ 30. _____ , or photographic memory, is more common in children.

_____ 31. _____ was Freud's explanation for unconscious forgetting.

_____ 32. Numbers are examples of units of thought called _____ .

_____ 33. _____ thinking depends on symbols, concepts, and rules.

_____ 34. Problem solving depends on the use of _____ .

_____ 35. _____ is the inability to imagine new functions for familiar objects.

Directions: Match each person or term in the left column with the best association. Write the letter of the association in the space provided. (2 points each)

_____ 36. short-term memory

_____ 37. sensory storage

_____ 38. George Miller

_____ 39. recognition

_____ 40. eidetic memory

_____ 41. mnemonic devices

_____ 42. proactive interference

_____ 43. image

_____ 44. nondirected thought

_____ 45. retroactive interference

a. blockage by new material

b. blockage by old material

c. daydreams

d. fraction of a second

e. memory aids

f. multiple-choice test

g. photographic memory

h. 7 units

i. active rehearsal

j. unit of thought

Directions: Answer the following questions in the space provided. (5 points each)

46. Describe the techniques used in improving memory.

_____

_____

_____

_____

_____

_____

_____

_____

_____

_____

47. Discuss some of the reasons for forgetting.

_____

_____

_____

_____

_____

_____

_____

_____

_____

_____

_____

CHAPTER 3 Test
Form B

MEMORY AND THOUGHT

Directions: In the space at the left, write the letter of the choice that best completes the statement or answers the question. (2 points each)

_____ 1. Which of the following is not one of the three basic steps of information processing?
    a. input
    b. selective attention
    c. output
    d. central processing

_____ 2. Which of the following is the most active form of memory retrieval?
    a. recognition
    b. recall
    c. reproduction
    d. recombination

_____ 3. A symbol used to represent a class of objects is called a(n)
    a. rule
    b. concept
    c. image
    d. set

_____ 4. The storing and sorting of information in the brain is called
    a. input
    b. nondirected thinking
    c. central processing
    d. none of the above

_____ 5. While playing tennis a scientist realizes the solution to a problem. This is called
    a. directed thinking
    b. symbolic thinking
    c. problem solving
    d. nondirected thinking

_____ 6. Which of the following does not apply to directed thinking?
    a. rules
    b. concepts
    c. symbols
    d. images

_____ 7. Metacognition is a strategy in which you think about
    a. thinking
    b. insight
    c. mnemonic devices
    d. retroactive interference

_____ 8. "Mass remains constant despite changes in appearance" is a
  a. concept
  b. rule
  c. symbol
  d. image

_____ 9. Mentally rearranging parts in order to find a novel solution is called
  a. functional fixedness
  b. flexibility
  c. set thinking
  d. recombination

_____ 10. Goal-directed thinking is
  a. nondirected
  b. imagery
  c. systematic
  d. divergent

Directions: Place a + in the space at the left of each true statement. Place a 0 at the left of each false statement. (2 points each)

_____ 11. The attenuation theory holds that we can process only one channel of information at a time.

_____ 12. Psychologists usually distinguish among three kinds of memory.

_____ 13. Nondirected thinking depends on images.

_____ 14. The symbol is the most primitive unit of thought.

_____ 15. Eidetic memory, or photographic memory, is more common in children than in adults.

_____ 16. A person may subconsciously block bad memories.

_____ 17. Sperling demonstrated the phenomenon of long-term memory.

_____ 18. Short-term memory is a passive storage system.

_____ 19. In retroactive interference an old memory blocks out a new one.

_____ 20. The most common symbols in thinking are words.

Directions: In the space at the left, write the term or terms that best complete the statement. (2 points each)

_____ 21. Information is any event that tends to reduce _____ .

_____ 22. Mnemonic devices are techniques to _____ information.

_____ 23. A(n) _____ is the most primitive unit of thought.

_____ 24. When a symbol is used as a label for a class of objects, it is called a(n)_____ .

_____ 25. Short-term memory can hold about _____ units.

_____ 26. _____ memory is our knowledge of language, including its rules, words, and meanings.

_____ 27. Metacognition is thinking about _____ .

_____ 28. A problem-solving strategy that becomes a habit is referred to as a(n)_____ .

_____ 29. _____ refers to memory blockage by new or old material.

_____ 30. _____ is the ability to use information in such a way that the result is original and meaningful.

_____ 31. Rearranging the elements of a problem is called _____ .

_____ 32. The most complex unit of thought is the _____ .

_____ 33. _____ refers to the idea and action that result from central processing.

_____ 34. _____ is the information people receive from their senses.

_____ 35. The sudden emergence of a solution by recombination is _____ .

Directions: Match each term in the left column with the best association. Write the letter of the association in the space provided. (2 points each)

_____ **36.** chunking

a. storing and sorting information in the brain

_____ **37.** central processing

b. perceiving related items as a unit

_____ **38.** episodic memory

c. memory of our own life

_____ **39.** prospagnosia

d. advocated attenuation theory

_____ **40.** confabulation

e. inability to recognize familiar faces

_____ **41.** selective attention

f. remembering events that did not happen

_____ **42.** rehearsal

g. advocated selection theory

_____ **43.** feature extraction

h. means to keep information in short-term memory

_____ **44.** Broadbent

i. identifying and analyzing specific elements of an input

_____ **45.** Treisman

j. focusing awareness on a limited segment of the total input

Directions: Answer the following questions on a separate sheet of paper. (5 points each)

46. Discuss creativity and the basic parts of this process.

47. Using examples, compare sensory storage, short-term memory, and long-term memory.

CHAPTER 4 Test

BODY AND BEHAVIOR

Form A

Directions: In the space at the left, write the letter of the choice that best completes the statement or answers the question. (2 points each)

_____ 1. The intensity of a sensation is determined by the
    a. amount of time it takes the signal to reach the somatosensory cortex in the brain
    b. number of neurons reacting
    c. autonomic nervous system
    d. length of the sensory nerve receiving the stimulation

_____ 2. The _____ nervous system does not belong in this grouping.
    a. autonomic   **b.** parasympathetic
    c. sympathetic   **d.** central

_____ 3. The EEG monitors
    a. electrical activity of the brain
    b. electrical activity of individual neurons
    c. the functioning of the hypothalamus
    d. electrical activity in the endocrine system

_____ 4. In an epileptic seizure
    a. the corpus callosum fails to transmit impulses
    b. the reticular formation is destroyed
    c. the endocrine system overwhelms the cerebellum
    d. abnormal electrical activity in one part of the brain spreads to larger areas

_____ 5. Evolution applies to
    a. anatomy
    b. physiology
    c. behavior
    d. all of the above

_____ 6. The brain and spinal cord make up the
    a. somatic nervous system
    b. hypothalamus
    c. central nervous system
    d. autonomic nervous system

_____ 7. The autonomic nervous system regulates the action of the
    a. somatic nervous system
    b. central nervous system
    c. involuntary muscles and organs
    d. voluntary skeletal muscles

_____ 8. The nervous system and the endocrine system
   a. release hormones into the bloodstream
   b. amplify voltages produced by neurons
   c. protect the spinal cord
   d. send information to and from the brain

_____ 9. Sociobiologists see their intellectual ancestry in
   a. Galton
   b. Darwin
   c. Tinbergen
   d. Lorenz

_____ 10. The first to preach the importance of nature in the modern era was
   a. Watson
   b. Wilson
   c. Galton
   d. Skinner

Directions: Place a + in the space at the left of each true statement. Place a 0 at the left of each false statement. (2 points each)

_____ 11. The interneurons are gaps between neurons.

_____ 12. The cerebral cortex guides one's biological needs.

_____ 13. Fixed action patterns are one kind of instinct.

_____ 14. Posture and balance are controlled by the cerebellum.

_____ 15. Dizygotic twins share the same genes.

_____ 16. The adult human brain weights approximately three pounds.

_____ 17. The thyroid gland is the master gland of the endocrine system.

_____ 18. Hippocrates was one of the first to notice the relationship between head injuries and disturbed thought.

_____ 19. Damage to the spinal cord could result in paralysis.

_____ 20. The sympathetic nervous system's purpose is to conserve energy.

_____ 21. The hypothalamus is the great relay center of the brain.

_____ 22. Visual information goes to the auditory lobes.

_____ 23. In right-handed people, the right hemisphere is involved in spatial tasks.

_____ 24. The EEG measures the flow of hormones in the body.

_____ 25. Galton concluded that environment was the reason for genius.

Directions: In the space at the left, write the term or terms that best complete the statement. (2 points each)

_____ 26. Messages are sent to the muscles from the brain by _____ .

_____ 27. The _____ nervous system works to conserve energy.

_____ 28. The hindbrain includes the medulla, cerebellum, and _____ .

_____ 29. The band of nerves that connects the hemispheres of the brain is the _____ .

_____ 30. Glands release _____ into the bloodstream, which causes breathing and heartbeat to increase.

_____ 31. The _____ hemisphere controls speech in most people.

_____ 32. Brain surgery aimed at changing an individual's thoughts and actions is called _____ .

_____ 33. A red belly is a(n) _____ for a stickleback fish to attack.

_____ 34. _____ twins develop from a single fertilized egg.

_____ 35. _____ is short for phenylketonuria, a genetic defect resulting in mental retardation.

Directions: Match each person or term in the left column with the best association. Write the letter of the association in the space provided. (2 points each)

_____ 36. cerebral cortex

_____ 37. thalamus

_____ 38. effectors

_____ 39. Wilson

_____ 40. lobes

_____ 41. electrode

_____ 42. hypothalamus

_____ 43. EEG

_____ 44. ethology

_____ 45. left hemisphere

a. type of wire

b. hormone monitor

c. major relay center

d. outer layer of the forebrain

e. measures electrical activity in brain

f. study of natural behavior patterns

g. sociobiology

h. speech center

i. regions of the brain

j. work muscles and glands

Directions: Answer the following questions on a separate sheet of paper. (5 points each)

46. Briefly describe how messages are transmitted to and from the brain.

47. Discuss the value of studying animals to gain knowledge of human behavior.

CHAPTER
4

Test

BODY AND BEHAVIOR

Form B

Directions: In the space at the left, write the letter of the choice that best completes the statement or answers the question. (2 points each)

_____ 1. The _____ gives you the ability to learn and store complex information.
a. reticular activating system
b. subcortex
c. cerebral cortex
d. spinal cord

_____ 2. All of the following are parts of the brain except the
a. hindbrain
b. EEG
c. forebrain
d. midbrain

_____ 3. Damage to the left hemisphere of the cerebral cortex will lead to
a. permanent loss of speech in children and adults
b. loss of spatial relations
c. temporary loss of speech in children and adults
d. permanent loss of speech in adults and temporary loss in children

_____ 4. Pleasure and pain centers have been located in the brain using the technique of
a. recording
b. stimulation
c. lesions
d. split-brain operation

_____ 5. Studies of the effects of genes on humans have focused on all of the following except
a. mental illness
b. personality
c. I.Q.
d. reaction time

_____ 6. Motor and sensory areas of the cerebral cortex are coordinated by the
a. association areas
b. hypothalamus
c. corpus callosum
d. thalamus

_____ 7. Violent rhesus monkeys become passive after researchers removed part of the
a. cerebellum
b. temporal lobe
c. cerebral cortex
d. adrenal glands

_____ 8. The endocrine system sends chemical messages called
   a. PKU
   b. synapses
   c. lesions
   d. hormones

_____ 9. Sociobiologists explain aggression in terms of
   a. conditioning
   b. modeling
   c. genetic advantage
   d. Freudian principles

_____ 10. Regions of the brain are referred to as
   a. lesions
   b. auditory system
   c. lobes
   d. skeletal muscles

Directions: Place a + in the space at the left of each true statement. Place a 0 at the left of each false statement. (2 points each)

_____ 11. The brain and spinal cord make up the peripheral nervous system.

_____ 12. Neurotransmitters cross the synapses.

_____ 13. Lesions are regions of the brain.

_____ 14. The endocrine system produces chemicals called hormones.

_____ 15. EEGs can be used to monitor brain malfunctions.

_____ 16. The pituitary gland acts as the master gland.

_____ 17. The brain is part of the peripheral nervous system.

_____ 18. The somatic nervous system controls involuntary muscles.

_____ 19. Ethologists study the natural behavior patterns of different species of animals.

_____ 20. The reticular activating system serves to alert the brain to incoming signals.

_____ 21. The cerebral cortex is less than a half-inch thick, but has a large surface area.

_____ 22. The pons houses the higher thinking processes.

_____ 23. About 60 percent of people are right handed.

_____ 24. Too much thyroxin makes people feel lethargic.

_____ 25. Studies indicate that schizophrenia is totally genetic in origin.

Directions: In the space at the left, write the term or terms that best complete the statement. (2 points each)

_____ 26. Chemical transmitters carry messages across gaps between neurons called _____ .

_____ 27. The spinal cord is protected by _____ .

_____ 28. Along with the thalamus, the _____ allows the brain to register some stimuli and filter out others.

_____ 29. The _____ areas of the brain mediate between sensory and motor areas.

_____ 30. The two hemispheres of the cortex are connected by the _____ .

_____ 31. The "master gland" of the endocrine system is the _____ .

_____ 32. Fixed action patterns are an example of a(n) _____ .

_____ 33. _____ draws from the disciplines of biology, anthropology, and psychology.

_____ 34. Evidence exists that schizophrenia is at least partially _____ .

_____ 35. Phenylketonuria can be controlled by _____ .

Directions: Match each person or term in the left column with the best association. Write the letter of the association in the space provided. (2 points each)

_____ **36.** PET

_____ **37.** epilepsy

_____ **38.** Darwin

_____ **39.** schizophrenia

_____ **40.** PKU

_____ **41.** cerebellum

_____ **42.** adrenal glands

_____ **43.** corpus callosum

_____ **44.** autonomic nervous system

_____ **45.** somatic nervous system

a. connection between hemispheres of brain

b. part of nervous system that controls automatic or involuntary actions

c. most common form of mental illness

d. theory of evolution

e. genetic disorder

f. became active when a person is angry or frightened

g. part of nervous system that controls voluntary action

h. part of hindbrain; helps central posture and balance

i. seizure disorder

j. technique used to locate tumors and seizure activity

Directions: Answer the following questions. Use a separate sheet of paper if necessary. (5 points each)

46. Discuss some of the difficulties in resolving the nature-nurture problem.

47. Explain some of the techniques used in exploring the brain.

 **Test** Form A

SENSATION AND PERCEPTION

Directions: In the space at the left, write the letter of the choice that best completes the statement or answers the question. (2 points each)

_____ 1. The perception of color is a function of
   a. decibel level   **c.** wavelength
   b. brightness   **d.** intensity

_____ 2. Specialized receptor cells responsible for night vision are called
   a. lenses   **b.** cones
   c. pupils   **c.** rods

_____ 3. The absolute threshold is the amount of energy a subject can experience _____ percent of the time.
   a. 100   **c.** 75
   b. 50   **d.** 25

_____ 4. In addition to our other senses, we have vestibular and _____ internal senses.
   a. olfactory   **c.** stereopsis
   b. auditory   **d.** kinesthetic

_____ 5. Pain experienced in an area away from the actual source is called _____ pain.
   a. illusory   **c.** hallucinatory
   b. referred   **d.** phantom limb

_____ 6. Which of the following is not a Gestalt principle?
   a. proximity   **c.** similarity
   b. continuity   **d.** illusion

_____ 7. You do not constantly feel your clothing on your body because of _____ .
   a. Weber's Law   **c.** sensory adaptation
   b. kinesthesis   **d.** difference threshold

_____ 8. Color blindness
   a. affects more men than women
   b. is a hereditary defect affecting more women than men
   c. is due to a deficiency of rods
   d. is due to a deficiency in the optic nerve

_____ 9. Smell receptors send messages to the brain via the _____ nerve.
   a. optic   **c.** olfactory
   b. auditory   **d.** vestibular

_____ 10. Filling in gaps in what our senses tell us is called
   a. proximity   **c.** perceptual inference
   b. figure-ground perception   **d.** perceptual constancies

Directions: Place a + in the space at the left of each true statement. Place a 0 at the left of each false statement. (2 points each)

_____ **11.** Any change in the environment to which the organism responds is called a stimulus.

_____ **12.** We have more than five senses.

_____ **13.** Sensations can combine with your past experience to yield a perception.

_____ **14.** Signal-detection theory studies the relationship between motivation, sensitivity, and decision making.

_____ **15.** Perceptual inference is largely an unconscious process.

_____ **16.** The organization of sensory experience into meaningful wholes is called sensation.

_____ **17.** Frequency and intensity are examples of sensory experiences.

_____ **18.** The amount of stimulus change necessary to produce a change in experience is the same for all the senses.

_____ **19.** The decision-making process in the perceptual system is conscious.

_____ **20.** Light enters the eye through the lens.

_____ **21.** The rods require more light than the cones to respond.

_____ **22.** Any sound over 60 decibels damages hearing.

_____ **23.** In humans smell and taste are matters of survival.

_____ **24.** The ability to recognize different people occurs at about two months.

_____ **25.** The fact that a friend walking toward you does not appear to change in size is an example of distance constancy.

Directions: In the space at the left, write the term or terms that best complete the statement. (2 points each)

_____ **26.** The interpretation of stimuli such as colors, sounds, smells, and taste is called _____ .

_____ **27.** Any change in the environment to which an organism responds is called a(n) _____ .

_____ **28.** Under ideal conditions the senses have very _____ absolute thresholds.

_____ 29. The _____ threshold is the smallest magnitude of a stimulus that can be detected half the time.

_____ 30. The _____ contains the light-sensitive receptor cells that allow us to see light and color.

_____ 31. The combination of the two images from our eyes into one is _____ .

_____ 32. Loudness is measured in _____ .

_____ 33. Scientists say that taste is made up of a total of _____ primary qualities.

_____ 34. _____ , continuity, and similarity are three basic principles of perceptual organization.

_____ 35. People perceive objects as the same size, whether they are far or near. This is an example of perceptual _____ .

Directions: Match each term in the left column with the best association. Write the letter of the association in the space provided. (2 points each)

_____ 36. color

_____ 37. difference threshold

_____ 38. Weber's law

_____ 39. cones

_____ 40. color deficiency

_____ 41. decibel

_____ 42. pitch

_____ 43. Gestalt psychologists

_____ 44. motion parallax

_____ 45. Rhine

a. daytime vision

b. depth perception

c. frequency of sound

d. hereditary defect

e. just noticeable difference

f. parapsychology

g. perception

h. proportion

i. unit of loudness

j. wavelength of light

Directions: Answer the following questions in the space provided. (5 points each)

46. Explain Weber's law using at least one example.

_____

_____

_____

_____

_____

_____

_____

_____

_____

_____

47. Discuss how the process of perception comes from sensory input. In your discussion, include explanations of perceptual inference, Gestalt laws, and constancy.

_____

_____

_____

_____

_____

_____

_____

_____

_____

_____

_____

Test

SENSATION AND PERCEPTION

Form B

CHAPTER 5

Directions: In the space at the left, write the letter of the choice that best completes the statement or answers the question. (2 points each)

_____ 1. The point at which we can discriminate two stimuli is called
   a. difference threshold
   b. absolute threshold
   c. Weber's Law
   d. terminal threshold

_____ 2. The _____ nerve transmits neural messages of sound vibrations to the brain.
   a. optic   **c.** olfactory
   b. auditory   **d.** semicircular

_____ 3. The structure that focuses light on the retina is the
   a. rods   **c.** olfactory nerve
   b. cones   **d.** lens

_____ 4. The absolute threshold is the amount of energy a subject can experience _____ percent of the time.
   a. 100   **c.** 75
   b. 50   **d.** 25

_____ 5. Weber's law is used to measure
   a. absolute thresholds   **c.** difference thresholds
   b. signal detection thresholds **d.** the response of the cones

_____ 6. Figure-ground perception is the ability to distinguish between
   a. close and distant objects   **c.** black and white
   b. figure and ground   **d.** reality and hallucination

_____ 7. Which of the following statements is true?
   a. color blindness affects more men than women
   b. color blindness is a hereditary defect affecting more women than men
   c. color blindness is due to a deficiency of rods
   d. color blindness is due to a deficiency in the optic nerve

_____ 8. Which of the following is not part of signal-detection theory?
   a. adaptation   **c.** decision making
   b. motivation   **d.** sensitivity

_____ 9. Light enters the eye through the
   a. retina   **c.** pupil
   b. lens   **d.** cornea

_____ 10. The semicircular canals are part of which system?
   a. auditory   **c.** optic
   b. vestibular   **d.** olfactory

Directions: Place a + in the space at the left of each true statement. Place a 0 at the left of each false statement. (2 points each)

_____ **11.** Absolute thresholds are set and invariable.

_____ **12.** Stereopsis is seeing depth as a result of retinal disparity.

_____ **13.** In order to create a cold sensation, a stimulus must have a temperature less than that of the skin.

_____ **14.** The vestibular nerve joins the optic nerve to the brain.

_____ **15.** Researchers can easily verify ESP results.

_____ **16.** The brightness of a stimulus is a function of its wavelength.

_____ **17.** The amount of stimulus change necessary to produce a change in experience is the same for all the senses.

_____ **18.** Our senses adjust to a constant level of stimulation.

_____ **19.** Hearing is the most studied of all the senses.

_____ **20.** The optic nerve goes from the eye to the brain.

_____ **21.** The cones are the part of the visual system sensitive to color.

_____ **22.** Smell is transmitted to the brain by the olfactory nerve.

_____ **23.** The fact that a friend walking toward you does not appear to change in size is an example of illusion constancy.

_____ **24.** Perception is basically a passive process.

_____ **25.** Figure-ground relationships only occur in vision.

Directions: In the space at the left, write the term or terms that best complete the statement. (2 points each)

_____ **26.** The _____ threshold is the smallest change in a physical stimulus that can be detected in half the trials.

_____ **27.** The study of the relationship between stimuli from the world and sensory experiences is called _____ .

_____ **28.** The ability to distinguish shades of red is an example of the _____ threshold.

_____ 29. The relationship between the magnitude of a stimulus and the amount of change necessary to see a difference is part of _____ .

_____ 30. There are _____ rods than cones in the retina.

_____ 31. The _____ nerve conveys sound impulses to the brain.

_____ 32. _____ and _____ are known as the chemical senses.

_____ 33. Pain does not easily _____ to stimulation.

_____ 34. According to Weber's law, the stronger a stimulus is, the _____ the change required for an observer to notice the change.

_____ 35. Misrepresentations of reality are called visual _____ .

Directions: Match each person or term in the left column with the best association. Write the letter of the association in the space provided. (2 points each)

_____ 36. pupil

_____ 37. rods

_____ 38. optic nerve

_____ 39. constancy

_____ 40. kinesthesis

_____ 41. referred pain

_____ 42. signal-detection

_____ 43. auditory nerve

_____ 44. subliminal advertising

_____ 45. extrasensory perception

a. sense of movement and body position

b. receptor cells in retina

c. carries impulses from inner ear to brain

d. sensation of pain in area away from the actual source

e. messages presented below normal threshold of detection

f. tendency to perceive certain objects in the same way

g. ability to gain information by some means other than the ordinary senses

h. carries impulses from retina to the brain

i. theory that summarizes mathematical relationship between motivation, sensitivity, and sensation

j. opening in the iris

Directions: Answer the following questions. Use a separate sheet of paper if necessary. (5 points each)

46. Discuss the physiology of vision.

_____

_____

_____

_____

_____

_____

_____

_____

_____

_____

47. Discuss and illustrate the concept of absolute and difference thresholds.

_____

_____

_____

_____

_____

_____

_____

_____

_____

_____

CHAPTER 6 Test

Form A

MOTIVATION AND EMOTION

Directions: In the space at the left, write the letter of the choice that best completes the statement or answers the question. (2 points each)

_____ 1. In the Harlow study, the monkeys preferred
   a. the mother that fed them
   b. the terry cloth mother
   c. the wire mother
   d. all mothers equally

_____ 2. Horner found that fear of success was greatest in
   a. women of average intelligence
   b. men of average intelligence
   c. women of above average intelligence
   d. men of above average intelligence

_____ 3. Dr. Jones is a psychologist who explains motivation in terms of underlying physiological states. He is most likely a follower of _____ theory.
   a. drive reduction
   b. social learning
   c. actualization
   d. need to achieve

_____ 4. Studies have shown that high achievers prefer to be associated with
   a. experts who will help them achieve
   b. friendly people
   c. low achievers
   d. aggressive people

_____ 5. Pleasure obtained from stimulation is overlooked by _____ theory.
   a. social learning
   b. drive reduction
   c. actualization
   d. cognitive

_____ 6. The focus of the Schachter and Singer experiment described in the text was
   a. perception
   b. appraisal
   c. drive reduction
   d. emotion

_____ 7. The "hierarchy of needs" was developed by
   a. Murray
   b. Maslow
   c. Horner
   d. McClelland

_____ **8.** The basic needs according to Maslow are called _____ needs.
    a. fundamental
    b. psychological
    c. self-actualization
    d. homeostatic

_____ **9.** Which of the following is a self-actualization need?
    a. feeling safe and secure
    b. being accepted and belonging
    c. having food and shelter
    d. fulfilling one's unique potential

_____ **10.** Darwin argued that people from different cultures express basic feelings
    a. in the same ways
    b. in different ways
    c. in the same ways except for facial expressions, which differ
    d. depending upon their sex

_____ **11.** Studies on obese individuals indicate that
    a. they use internal cues to eat
    b. the psychological realm plays a small part
    c. they use external cues to eat
    d. they block out external cues

_____ **12.** In Maslow's hierarchy, the need to receive and give love is a _____ need.
    a. homeostatic
    b. fundamental
    c. psychological
    d. self-actualization

_____ **13.** The "flight" reaction of the sympathetic nervous system was first described by
    a. William James
    b. Philip Bard
    c. Charles Darwin
    d. Walter Cannon

Directions: Place a + in the space at the left of each true statement. Place a 0 at the left of each false statement. (2 points each)

_____ **14.** Research on motivation focuses on the "how" of behavior.

_____ **15.** When body temperature goes above a certain point, the blood vessels constrict.

_____ **16.** Hunger is a homeostatic drive.

_____ **17.** Drive reduction theory is associated with Harry Harlow.

_____ **18.** Murray's theory of personality identified sixteen basic needs.

_____ **19.** Maslow believes that very few people reach the level of self-actualization needs.

_____ **20.** Darwin argued that all people express certain basic feelings in the same way.

_____ **21.** Obese individuals are more sensitive to internal cues.

_____ **22.** Horner discovered that fear of success was strongest in women of average intelligence.

_____ **23.** The hypothalamus regulates food intake.

_____ **24.** The James-Lange theory states that bodily changes trigger emotions.

_____ **25.** Solomon and Corbit proposed an opponent-process theory of emotion.

Directions: In the space at the left, write the term or terms that best complete the statement. (2 points each)

_____ **26.** Motivation is inferred from _____ behavior.

_____ **27.** The _____ hypothalamus initiates food-eating behavior.

_____ **28.** The ventromedial hypothalamus is _____ active in warm temperatures.

_____ **29.** Schachter demonstrated that obese individuals respond to _____ cues.

_____ **30.** Drive reduction theory is associated with the psychologist _____ .

_____ **31.** Most of Murray's basic needs are _____ motives, rather than biological.

_____ **32.** McClelland has found that people with a high need to achieve tend not to be _____ sensitive.

_____ **33.** The consequences of striving for goals evoke _____ .

_____ **34.** Even the most basic emotions can be changed by _____ .

_____ **35.** The Cannon-Bard theory localizes the part of the lower brain called the _____ as the seat of emotions.

Directions: Match each person, team, or term in the left column with the best association. Write the letter of the association in the space provided. (2 points each)

_____ 36. lateral hypothalamus

_____ 37. Hull

_____ 38. Harlow

_____ 39. James-Lange

_____ 40. Schachter-Singer

_____ 41. Maslow

_____ 42. ventromedial hypothalamus

_____ 43. McClelland

_____ 44. Horner

_____ 45. Cannon-Bard

a. begin hunger drive

b. cognitive theory of emotions

c. drive reduction theory

d. early theory of emotions

e. end hunger drive

f. fear of success

g. hierarchy of needs

h. need to achieve

i. surrogate mothers

j. thalamus as center of emotions

Directions: Answer the following questions. Use a separate sheet of paper if necessary. (5 points each)

46. Discuss and comment on Maslow's theory of needs.

_____

_____

_____

_____

_____

47. Discuss the relationship between motivation and emotions.

_____

_____

_____

_____

_____

_____

_____

Test

MOTIVATION AND EMOTION

Form B

Directions: In the space at the left, write the letter of the choice that best completes the statement or answers the question. (2 points each)

_____ 1. Studies on obese individuals indicate that
    a. they use internal cues to eat
    b. the psychological realm plays a small part
    c. they use external cues to eat
    d. they block out external cues

_____ 2. _____ theory states that psychological needs drives an organism to act in certain ways until its needs are satisfied.
    a. The James-Lange
    b. Drive reduction
    c. Signal detection
    d. none of the above

_____ 3. The tendency of organisms to correct deviations from their normal state is called
    a. motivation
    b. expectancy value
    c. homeostasis
    d. innate behavior

_____ 4. McClelland used the TAT as a tool to
    a. prove extrinsic motivation
    b. test polygraph tests
    c. measure achievement motivation
    d. test the opponent-process theory

_____ 5. Anorexia nervosa and bulimia are
    a. not serious disorders
    b. two terms for the same disorder
    c. found mostly in young males
    d. found mostly in young females

_____ 6. "We feel sorry because we cry" is a statement attributed to the _____ theory.
    a. Cannon-Bard
    b. James-Lange
    c. Schachter-Singer
    d. Darwin

_____ 7. The James-Lange theory is best described as a(n)
    a. social hierarchy
    b. opponent-process theory
    c. cognitive theory
    d. physiological theory

_____ **8.** High achievers prefer to be associated with
  a. their families
  b. experts who help them achieve
  c. people who are inferior to them
  d. friendly people

_____ **9.** Which of the following describes a man responding to an external cue?
  a. He eats because he finds something good to eat
  b. He eats because he is hungry
  c. He eats more during the summer
  d. none of the above

_____ **10.** The concept of the motive to avoid success is associated with
  a. Murray
  b. Horner
  c. Maslow
  d. McClelland

_____ **11.** The differences in emotions that we find in various cultures are due to
  a. climate
  b. learning
  c. maturation
  d. genetics

_____ **12.** A polygraph is also known as a(n)
  a. lie detector
  b. EKG
  c. intrinsic drive
  d. homeostatic effect

_____ **13.** The needs at the top of Maslow's hierarchy are _____ needs.
  a. self-actualization
  b. psychological
  c. fundamental
  d. homeostatic

Directions: Place a + in the space at the left of each true statement. Place a 0 at the left of each false statement. (2 points each)

_____ **14.** All motives can be reduced to physiological needs.

_____ **15.** If the lateral hypothalamus is stimulated, an organism will stop eating.

_____ **16.** Motivation cannot be directly observed.

_____ **17.** McClelland's main research tool was the Rorschach test.

_____ **18.** The lateral hypothalamus is more active in cold temperatures.

_____ **19.** McClelland believes that we should all be trained to be high achievers.

_____ **20.** The level of sugar in the blood is the sole factor that causes the hypothalamus to act.

_____ **21.** McClelland was interested in trying to change emotional levels.

_____ **22.** Maslow put psychological needs at the base of his hierarchy of human needs.

_____ **23.** According to Maslow, security is a fundamental need.

_____ **24.** Horner discovered that women have little fear of success.

_____ **25.** A person who is in a good mood is more likely to be helpful.

Directions: In the space at the left, write the term or terms that best complete the statement. (2 points each)

_____ **26.** The state of physiological balance is called _____ .

_____ **27.** The _____ hypothalamus provides the stop signals for eating.

_____ **28.** _____ theory is associated with Hull.

_____ **29.** According to Hull, when random behaviors reduce a drive, the organism acquires a(n) _____ .

_____ **30.** The lateral hypothalamus is _____ active in warm temperatures.

_____ **31.** The _____ was McClelland's basic research tool.

_____ **32.** Needs for competence and achievement are _____ needs according to Maslow's hierarchy of needs.

_____ **33.** Studies indicate that certain facial expression tend to be _____ , or not learned.

_____ **34.** "We feel afraid because we tremble" is an explanation offered by the _____ theory of emotions.

_____ **35.** _____ theorists claim body change and thinking work together to produce emotions.

Directions: Match each person or term in the left column with the best association. Write the letter of the association in the space provided. (2 points each)

_____ **36.** innate

a. projective test

_____ **37.** set-point

b. inherited

_____ **38.** TAT

c. task performed for external rewards

_____ **39.** polygraph

d. lie detector

_____ **40.** homeostasis

e. weight around which day-to-day weight tends to fluctuate

_____ **41.** bulimia

f. serious eating disorder

_____ **42.** intrinsic motivation

g. opponent-process theory

_____ **43.** extrinsic motivation

h. task performed for reasons other than external rewards

_____ **44.** Atkinson

i. expectancy-value theory

_____ **45.** Solomon-Corbit

j. tendency to correct imbalances and deviations from normal state

Directions: Answer the following questions on a separate sheet of paper. (5 points each)

46. Discuss and compare the physiological and cognitive theories of emotion.

47. Discuss the reasons why drive-reduction theory was abandoned as an explanation of all human motives.

CHAPTER 7 Test

ALTERED STATES OF CONSCIOUSNESS

Form A

Directions: In the space at the left, write the letter of the choice that best completes the statement or answers the question. (2 points each)

_____ 1. Hallucinations can be caused by
  a. drugs
  b. fatigue
  c. heightened emotional states
  d. all of the above

_____ 2. There are _____ stages of quiet sleep.
  a. four
  b. two
  c. three
  d. seven

_____ 3. Which of the following occurs during REM sleep?
  a. muscles relax
  b. absence of dreams
  c. deep sleep
  d. dreaming

_____ 4. The most potent hallucinogenic drug is
  a. marijuana
  b. LSD
  c. mescaline
  d. peyote

_____ 5. Freud felt that dreams
  a. are meaningless
  b. represent conscious wishes
  c. are uninterpretable
  d. are highly meaningful

_____ 6. Cocaine (crack), caffeine, and nicotine are addicting drugs that are
  a. stimulants
  b. depressants
  c. psychedelics
  d. none of the above

_____ 7. One of the most effective cures for insomnia involves
  a. behavior modification
  b. increasing the amount of REM sleep
  c. meditation
  d. sensory deprivation

_____ 8. _____ can be used to reduce high blood pressure.
  a. Blood-pressure biofeedback
  b. Meditation
  c. Muscle-tension feedback
  d. All of the above

_____ 9. The primary effects of alcohol are caused by the alcohol and
  a. social effects
  b. cigarettes
  c. hallucinogens
  d. depressants

_____ 10. The controversy regarding whether and how meditation works has focused on similar effects that can sometimes be achieved simply by
   a. hallucinating
   b. meditating
   c. relaxing
   d. being hypnotized

_____ 11. Stage_____ is the deepest stage of quiet sleep.
   a. I
   b. II
   c. III
   d. IV

_____ 12. After the stages of quiet sleep, you enter a more active type of sleep called
   a. Stage II
   b. Stage III
   c. REM sleep
   d. none of the above

_____ 13. A type of altered consciousness in which people become highly suggestible and do not use their critical thinking skills is called
   a. meditation
   b. Stage I sleep
   c. hypnosis
   d. biofeedback

_____ 14. Most psychologists would probably agree that hypnosis
   a. does not work
   b. has little to do with suggestibility
   c. reveals that people often have potential abilities that they do not use
   d. all of the above

_____ 15. Perceptions that have no direct external cause are referred to as
   a. hallucinations
   b. hypnotic states
   c. trance logic
   d. amnesia

_____ 16. Barbiturates, alcohol, and valium are classified as
   a. opiates
   b. inhalants
   c. stimulants
   d. depressants

_____ 17. Cocaine, alcohol, and narcotics
   a. have a high habituation potential
   b. may lead users to ever-increasing amounts
   c. have a high addiction potential
   d. all of the above

_____ 18. Short-term effects of marijuana use include
   a. distortion of thoughts
   b. nausea and anxiety
   c. rapid mood changes
   d. all of the above

Directions: Place a + in the space at the left of each true statement. Place a 0 at the left of each false statement. (2 points each)

_____ **19.** An altered state of consciousness is a quantitative change only.

_____ **20.** Hypnosis is a form of altered consciousness.

_____ **21.** Daydreams may involve mild hallucinations.

_____ **22.** Blood pressure generally increases under stress.

_____ **23.** Hallucinogens are found in plants.

_____ **24.** Behaviorism stresses the need to study the varied states of consciousness.

_____ **25.** Dreams correspond to a reasonably realistic time scale.

_____ **26.** Kleitman feels that dreams represent important unconscious processes.

_____ **27.** Hallucinogens were first discovered by researchers in the 1960s.

_____ **28.** The levels of adrenal and sexual hormones rise during REM sleep.

_____ **29.** Intervals of dreaming get longer as the night progresses.

_____ **30.** Anxious people have more nightmares than less-anxious people do.

Directions: In the space at the left, write the term or terms that best complete the statement. (2 points each)

_____ **31.** One reason for the popularity of behaviorism is that _____ proved difficult to study scientifically.

_____ **32.** Brain waves are measured by a(n) _____ .

_____ **33.** Bedwetting may occur during Stage _____ sleep.

_____ **34.** When people are awakened during REM sleep and asked to report dreams, the dreams tend to be _____ .

_____ **35.** A person denied sensory stimulation may be irritable, lose concentration, and may even _____ .

Directions: Match each person or term in the left column with the best association. Write the letter of the association in the space provided. (2 points each)

_____ 36. Stage IV sleep   a. belladonna

_____ 37. REM sleep   b. control of physiological processes

_____ 38. Freud   c. deep sleep

_____ 39. Barber   d. dream interpretation

_____ 40. Hebb   e. dream sleep

_____ 41. marijuana   f. hypnosis

_____ 42. hallucinogenic drug   g. relaxation response

_____ 43. biofeedback   h. sensory deprivation

_____ 44. Benson   i. flashback experiences

_____ 45. LSD   j. THC

Directions: Answer the following questions in the space provided. If necessary, continue on a separate sheet of paper. (5 points each)

46. Define hallucinations, and give examples of the various situations under which they may occur.

_____

_____

_____

_____

_____

47. Discuss and illustrate the relaxation responses.

_____

_____

_____

_____

_____

_____

 **Test** Form B

ALTERED STATES OF CONSCIOUSNESS

Directions: In the space at the left, write the letter of the choice that best completes the statement or answers the question. (2 points each)

_____ 1. Sleepwalking most likely occurs during which stage of sleep?
a. Stage I
b. Stage II
c. Stage III
d. Stage IV

_____ 2. Sensations or perceptions without any external cause are
a. illusions
b. delusions
c. hallucinations
d. daydreams

_____ 3. Michelle takes part in a sensory deprivation experiment. All of the following except _____ are probably going to occur during the experiment.
a. irritability
b. increased concentration
c. restlessness
d. emotional upset

_____ 4. Your brain becomes inactive during
a. REM sleep
b. deep sleep
c. hallucinations
d. none of the above

_____ 5. Which of the following is true of hypnosis?
a. it is similar to deep sleep
b. generally, the subject cannot be forced to do things against his or her will
c. the subject becomes less responsive to internal stress
d. the subject is unable to focus on one aspect of reality

_____ 6. Drugs whose main effect is to produce hallucinations are called
a. stimulants
b. hallucinogens
c. cannabis
d. depressants

_____ 7. Someone suffering tension headaches would achieve the strongest relief through
a. biofeedback
b. lowered blood pressure
c. meditation
d. hallucinations

_____ 8. _____ can be used to reduce high blood pressure.
a. Blood-pressure biofeedback
b. Meditation
c. Muscle-tension biofeedback
d. All of the above

_____ 9. The controversy regarding whether and how meditation works has focused on similar effects that can sometimes be achieved simply by
a. hallucinating
b. meditating
c. relaxing
d. being hypnotized

Directions: Place a + in the space at the left of each true statement. Place a 0 at the left of each false statement. (2 points each)

_____ 10. Stage IV is deep sleep.

_____ 11. The levels of adrenal and sexual hormones rise during REM sleep.

_____ 12. At certain stages during sleep, your brain becomes inactive.

_____ 13. Hypnosis puts the subject to sleep.

_____ 14. Delta waves are associated with Stage IV sleep.

_____ 15. Most people are likely to remember non-REM dreams.

_____ 16. Freud felt that dream symbols were universal.

_____ 17. The relationship between hypnotist and subject is one of domination.

_____ 18. Mescaline is the most potent hallucinogenic drug.

_____ 19. Dreams correspond to a reasonably realistic time scale.

_____ 20. The body and brain are active during the night.

_____ 21. During Stage IV sleep, an individual experiences rapid brain waves with high peaks and valleys.

_____ 22. Daydreaming is an important sign signalling psychological disturbance.

_____ 23. A person with a psychological addiction believes that he or she needs a substance in order to deal with daily stress.

_____ 24. Alcohol is a stimulant.

_____ 25. Although most people view alcohol as a depressant, its actual effects are those of a stimulant.

_____ 26. Relatively few people dream during the night.

_____ 27. Stage I sleep may be described as the state of transition between wakefulness and sleep.

_____ 28. Caffeine is an addictive stimulant found in coffee and other beverages.

_____ 29. Nicotine is an addictive stimulant present in cigarettes.

_____ 30. Barbiturates are addictive depressants.

Directions: In the space at the left, write the term or terms that best complete the statement. (2 points each)

_____ **31.** The most common state of altered consciousness is _____.

_____ **32.** During Stage _____ sleep, delta waves sweep the brain every second or so.

_____ **33.** Sexual and adrenal hormones increase during _____ sleep.

_____ **34.** Freud felt that the _____ of dreams is a private language.

_____ **35.** Caffeine affects the _____ nervous system.

Directions: Match each person or term in the left column with the best association. Write the letter of the association in the space provided. (2 points each)

_____ **36.** consciousness

_____ **37.** hallucinations

_____ **38.** hypertension

_____ **39.** hypnosis

_____ **40.** meditation

_____ **41.** posthypnotic suggestion

_____ **42.** Crick

_____ **43.** manifest content

_____ **44.** latent content

_____ **45.** Gilligan

a. naturally altered state of consciousness

b. suggestion made during a hypnotic trance

c. perceptions that have no direct external cause

d. dream matter that comes from events of the day

e. theory of dreams

f. studied 12 trance conditions

g. dream content that comes from a person's unconscious wishes

h. state of awareness

i. high levels of blood pressure

j. focusing attention

Directions: Answer the following questions in the space provided. If necessary, continue on a separate sheet of paper. (5 points each)

46. Discuss the uses of biofeedback in the treatment of physical ailments.

_____

_____

_____

_____

_____

_____

_____

_____

_____

_____

47. Discuss the research and theories on the nature of hypnosis.

_____

_____

_____

_____

_____

_____

_____

_____

_____

_____

CHAPTER 8 Test

Form A

INFANCY AND CHILDHOOD

Directions: In the space at the left, write the letter of the choice that best completes the statement or answers the question. (2 points each)

_____ 1. Which of the following helps an infant find the mother's breast?
  a. grasping reflex
  b. rooting reflex
  c. sucking reflex
  d. strong visual activity

_____ 2. Imprinting is
  a. slowly developed over months or years
  b. entirely based on learning
  c. sudden, within hours or a day
  d. maturational

_____ 3. A given quantity remains the same even though its container changes size and shape. This is the principle of
  a. solidity
  b. sameness
  c. conservation
  d. representational thought

_____ 4. Symbolic representation begins during the _____ stage.
  a. sensorimotor
  b. preoperational
  c. concrete operations
  d. formal operations

_____ 5. Which of the following was a cognitive developmental theorist?
  a. Bandura
  b. Erikson
  c. Kohlberg
  d. Freud

_____ 6. Which of the following is not true for infants?
  a. the world is seen as a blurry mass
  b. they demonstrate the grasping reflex
  c. they demonstrate the rooting reflex
  d. they are attuned to distinct edges

_____ 7. According to Piaget, which term refers to a child's attempt to understand something new by fitting it into an existing scheme of understanding?
  a. accommodation
  b. assimilation
  c. intuitive reasoning
  d. sensorimotor intelligence

_____ 8. Which of the following is true according to Piaget?
   a. thinking with words comes before thinking with action
   b. thinking with action precedes thinking with words
   c. thinking and language are the same
   d. symbolic thought precedes sensorimotor thought

_____ 9. Of the three steps in language acquisition, the last and most complex is
   a. meaning
   b. signs
   c. symbols
   d. grammar

_____ 10. Harlow found that in the use of surrogate mothers
   a. feeding was the primary basis of attachment
   b. touching was more important than feeding
   c. surrogate mothers led to healthier baby monkeys
   d. independence training is not necessary for healthy adjustment

_____ 11. Erikson's first stage of psychosocial development is
   a. trust vs. mistrust
   b. autonomy vs. doubt
   c. initiative vs. guilt
   d. industry vs. inferiority

_____ 12. The concept of imitation and social learning is associated with
   a. Kohlberg
   b. Erikson
   c. Freud
   d. Bandura

_____ 13. The desire for social approval characterizes stage _____ of Kohlberg's model.
   a. one
   b. three
   c. five
   d. six

Directions: Place a + in the space at the left of each true statement. Place a 0 at the left of each false statement. (2 points each)

_____ 14. The rooting reflex is a response to touch on the palm of the hand.

_____ 15. Piaget has been the leading researcher into the emotional development of children.

_____ 16. "Law and Order" characterizes stage four of the Kohlberg model of moral development.

_____ 17. Babies begin to form attachments to their mothers at about six months of age.

_____ 18. About 25 percent of all mentally retarded individuals have physically impaired brains.

_____ **19.** Developmental psychology covers the life span from birth to adolescence.

_____ **20.** Newborns can lift their heads.

_____ **21.** Newborns can change their behavior in response to the environment.

_____ **22.** According to Piaget, initial schemes include sucking and grasping.

_____ **23.** Piaget claims that children develop separation anxiety between the ages of two and five.

_____ **24.** Most children in grades 1-6 have achieved Piaget's stage of formal operation.

_____ **25.** Babbling comes before cooing for the human infant.

_____ **26.** Harlow's work demonstrated the importance of imprinting.

_____ **27.** Freud believed that boys and girls have different experiences in the first four years of life.

_____ **28.** Autonomy vs. doubt is Erikson's first stage of psychosocial development.

Directions: In the space at the left, write the term or terms that best complete the statement. (2 points each)

_____ **29.** If a newborn is touched around the mouth, it turns in the direction of the touch. This is the _____ reflex.

_____ **30.** For Piaget, intellectual development involves changes in the amount of information as well as in the _____ of thinking.

_____ **31.** During the _____ stage, thinking becomes abstract and hypothetical.

_____ **32.** The omission of certain words is typical of the speech of a young child and is called _____ speech.

_____ **33.** According to Freud, the young boy resolves the Oedipal conflict by _____ with the father.

_____ **34.** Intimacy vs. isolation is the conflict of early adulthood according to _____ .

_____ **35.** According to _____ theorists, much of children's play involves role playing.

Directions: Match each person or term in the left column with the best association. Write the letter of the association in the space provided. (2 points each)

_____ 36. maturation

_____ 37. Piaget

_____ 38. symbols

_____ 39. formal operational stage

_____ 40. Lorenz

_____ 41. Freud

_____ 42. Erikson

_____ 43. Bandura

_____ 44. Kohlberg

_____ 45. Harlow

a. adult thought

b. imprinting

c. internally programmed growth

d. modeling

e. moral development

f. mothering

g. Oedipal conflict

h. psychosocial stages

i. representational thought

j. stages of thinking

Directions: Answer the following questions on a separate sheet of paper. (5 points each)

46. Discuss the similarities and differences between the social learning theorists and the cognitive theorists in regard to the development of morality.

47. Discuss the applicability of animal research in the study of human emotional development.

CHAPTER 8 Test

Form B

INFANCY AND CHILDHOOD

Directions: In the space at the left, write the letter of the choice that best completes the statement or answers the question. (2 points each)

_____ 1. Piaget's research shows that
  a. full intelligence is present at birth
  b. intelligence is a quantitative change
  c. the sequence of the stages of intellectual growth do not vary
  d. the stages of intellectual growth are a function of the environment

_____ 2. The child's first experience of not getting what he/she wants occurs during the _____ stage.
  a. anal
  b. oral
  c. phallic
  d. latency

_____ 3. Johnny has just identified with his father, whom he previously regarded as a threat. He most likely is at the end of the _____ stage.
  a. oral   c. phallic
  b. anal   d. genital

_____ 4. Mrs. Smith, a middle-aged woman, would be going through the _____ crisis, according to Erikson's theory.
  a. integrity vs. despair
  b. generativity vs. stagnation
  c. intimacy vs. isolation
  d. autonomy vs. doubt

_____ 5. Cognitive theorists believe that
  a. children are shaped by their environments
  b. sexual and aggressive drives underlie children's activities
  c. children will learn well if given the proper role models
  d. children actively shape their environments

_____ 6. An infant has developed object permanence. This means that he/she
  a. is attached to specific objects
  b. will see all objects as the same
  c. knows that an object exists even if he/she can't see it
  d. can find a hidden object

_____ 7. Which of the following terms includes all the others?
  a. assimilation
  b. schemes
  c. accommodation
  d. intellectual development

8. Mental retardation is
   a. an emotional rather than intellectual disability
   b. almost always due to brain damage
   c. most common in middle-class families
   d. primarily an intellectual rather than an emotional disability.

9. Bobby is a child who has just mastered the basics of language. He most likely is _____ years old.
   a. two
   b. four to five
   c. nine to ten
   d. three to four

10. Freud believed that children are born with _____ urges.
   a. social and dependent
   b. sexual but not aggressive
   c. aggressive but not sexual
   d. sexual and aggressive

11. Erikson's stage that corresponds to Freud's latency stage is
   a. identity vs. role confusion
   b. intimacy vs. isolation
   c. initiative vs. guilt
   d. the obeying of authority

12. For Kohlberg, morality depends upon
   a. the ability to see things from another person's point of view
   b. religious training
   c. proper parental models
   d. the obeying of authority

13. The "Golden Rule" is characteristic of stage(s) _____ of Kohlberg's model.
   a. four
   b. five
   c. six
   d. five and six

Directions: Place a + in the space at the left of each true statement. Place a 0 at the left of each false statement. (2 points each)

14. By eight months a child is physiologically ready to walk.

15. Separation anxiety characterizes the 10- to 12-month-old baby.

16. Changing our schemes to fit the characteristics of the world is called accommodation.

17. According to Freud, the first developmental stage is the anal stage.

18. Sublimation is prevalent during the phallic stage.

19. Evidence exists that newborns are perceptually attuned to distinct edges.

_____ **20.** Maturation is as important as learning during the first year.

_____ **21.** Piaget concluded that the difference between younger and older children is the amount of information they have.

_____ **22.** Object permanence usually develops within the first year.

_____ **23.** The preoperational stage usually occurs between about two and six years of age.

_____ **24.** Mental retardation refers to emotional, not intellectual, difficulties.

_____ **25.** The average two-year old has a vocabulary of about 50 words.

_____ **26.** Harlow discovered that the monkeys reared with surrogate mothers grew up with serious emotional problems.

_____ **27.** Freud theorizes that the Oedipal conflict occurs between the ages of three and five.

_____ **28.** For Erikson, adolescence is hallmarked by the conflict between identity and role confusion.

Directions: In the space at the left, write the term or terms that best complete the statement. (2 points each)

_____ **29.** The Swiss psychologist _____ proposed the most comprehensive theory of intellectual development.

_____ **30.** The awareness that things exist even if you can't see or touch them is called _____ .

_____ **31.** The rules for organization of symbols are called _____ .

_____ **32.** Learning the rules of behavior of one's culture is called _____ .

_____ **33.** Sublimation, characterizing the _____ stage, leads to a repression of sexual and aggressive drives.

_____ **34.** According to Erikson, the conflict between _____ and _____ is where the child learns self-control and self-assertion.

_____ **35.** In stage one of Kohlberg's model, children are totally _____ .

Directions: Match each person or term in the left column with the best association. Write the letter of the association in the space provided. (2 points each)

_____ 36. schemes

a. process of fitting objects and experiences into schemes for understanding

_____ 37. socialization

b. adjusting one's schemes to fit newly observed events and experiences

_____ 38. sublimation

c. process of learning rules of behavior of one's culture

_____ 39. rooting

d. plans for knowing

_____ 40. conservation

e. principle that a given quantity does not change when its appearance changes

_____ 41. accommodation

f. phase characterized by fear at caregiver's prolonged absence

_____ 42. assimilation

g. process of redirecting sexual impulses into learning tasks

_____ 43. imprinting

h. realization that an object exists even when it cannot be seen

_____ 44. separation anxiety

i. infants' response in turning toward source of touching

_____ 45. object permanence

j. process of forming attachment to objects or organisms very early in life

Directions: Answer the following questions on a separate sheet of paper. (5 points each)

46. Discuss the stages of intellectual growth delineated by Piaget.

47. Discuss and illustrate some of the capabilities with which the newborn child enters the world.

CHAPTER 9 Test

ADOLESCENCE

Form A

Directions: In the space at the left, write the letter of the choice that best completes the statement or answers the question. (2 points each)

_____ 1. The concept of identity moratorium is associated with
    a. Piaget   **c.** Marcia
    b. Levinson   **d.** Bem

_____ 2. The term "identity crisis" is associated with
    a. Levinson   **c.** Erikson
    b. Piaget   **d.** Hall

_____ 3. Which of the following characterize adolescent thought?
    a. hypothetical propositions
    b. abstraction
    c. systematic experimentation
    d. all of the above

_____ 4. An adolescent who relies heavily on the suggestions of others in order to make commitments to important life matters can be described as an
    a. identity-confused adolescent
    b. identity-diffused adolescent
    c. identity-foreclosure adolescent
    d. identity-moratorium adolescent

_____ 5. Which of the following terms does not belong with the others?
    a. puberty   **c.** adolescence
    b. menarche   **d.** menopause

_____ 6. Jill, an incoming high school freshman, is most likely to join a group based on the dimension of
    a. sex   **c.** race
    b. age   **d.** appearance

_____ 7. Robert, a seventeen-year-old middle-class boy, is statistically most likely to be in the transition to _____ operational thinking.
    a. sensorimotor   **c.** concrete
    b. formal   **d.** preoperational

_____ 8. Rites of passage from one age or status to another are
    a. initiation rites   **c.** identity crisis
    b. preoperational   **d.** none of the above

_____ 9. In Jim's family the parents make all the ultimate decisions without consulting Jim. This might be considered a(n) _____ family.
    a. permissive   **c.** authoritarian
    b. laissez-faire   **d.** democratic

_____ **10.** Tommy, a typical adolescent, most likely will turn to peers for advice on
       a. marriage   **c.** music
       b. religion   **d.** educational plans

Directions: Place a + in the space at the left of each true statement. Place a 0 at the left of each false statement. (2 points each)

_____ **11.** Piaget felt that thinking patterns characteristic of adults emerge during adolescence.

_____ **12.** Hall portrayed adolescence as a time of storm and stress.

_____ **13.** Teens brought up in laissez-faire families seem to be the healthiest psychologically.

_____ **14.** Research indicates that boys who mature early have an advantage.

_____ **15.** Menarche occurs between the ages of 10 and 17.

_____ **16.** According to Kohlberg, the third stage of development is self-fulfilling prophecy.

_____ **17.** In some societies people move directly from childhood to adulthood.

_____ **18.** Formal operational thinking is less prevalent in some societies than in others.

_____ **19.** Sex roles result from biological inheritance.

_____ **20.** Most peer groups pose a threat to adult authority.

_____ **21.** Freud describes adolescent thought as formal operational thinking.

_____ **22.** Late maturing girls tend to get along more easily with their peers.

_____ **23.** Stage four individuals accept absolute ethical principles.

_____ **24.** Marcia distinguished between six adolescent personality types.

_____ **25.** All psychologists agree that adolescents experience an identity crisis.

Directions: In the space at the left, write the term or terms that best complete the statement. (2 points each)

_____ **26.** In _____ families, parents often give up their child-rearing responsibilities.

_____ **27.** According to _____ , building an identity is a task that is unique to adolescence.

_____ **28.** The psychologist _____ believed adolescence to be a period of storm and stress.

_____ 29. _____ is the biological end of childhood.

_____ 30. Adolescents growing up in _____ families tend to assume responsibility gradually.

_____ 31. A social group within a set is called a(n) _____ .

_____ 32. According to Kohlberg, individuals in Stage _____ accept absolute ethical principles.

_____ 33. _____ is describing reasons or making up excuses for failing.

_____ 34. Sandra Bem found that _____ people were more flexible.

_____ 35. In _____ families, adolescents participate in decisions that affect them.

Directions: Match each person or term in the left column with the best association. Write the letter of the association in the space provided. (2 points each)

_____ 36. adolescence   **a.** androgyny

_____ 37. puberty   **b.** biological end to childhood

_____ 38. laissez-faire families   **c.** belief that own actions can save the world

_____ 39. authoritarian families   **d.** children are often in control

_____ 40. clique   **e.** identity crisis

_____ 41. Erikson   **f.** parents are in total control

_____ 42. Bem   **g.** psychological stage

_____ 43. Bandura   **h.** set within a group

_____ 44. Hall   **i.** social learning theory of development

_____ 45. messianic complex   **j.** storm and stress

Directions: Answer the following questions in the space provided. (5 points each)

46. Discuss the conflicts faced by the adolescent.

_____

_____

_____

_____

_____

_____

_____

_____

_____

_____

47. Argue for or against the advantages of androgyny as defined by Bem.

_____

_____

_____

_____

_____

_____

_____

_____

_____

_____

_____

CHAPTER 9 Test

Form B

ADOLESCENCE

Directions: In the space at the left, write the letter of the choice that best completes the statement or answers the question. (2 points each)

_____ 1. The concept of identity achievement adolescents are associated with
    a. Piaget   **c.** Marcia
    b. Levinson   **d.** Bem

_____ 2. Independence, autonomy, and confidence characterize children raised in
    a. authoritarian families
    b. democratic families
    c. laissez-faire families
    d. permissive families

_____ 3. Sex identity results from
    a. cultural mores
    b. attitudes
    c. biological inheritance
    d. none of the above

_____ 4. Which of the following statements regarding family conflict is not true?
    a. Large middle-class families experience more conflict than smaller middle-class families.
    b. Conflicts occur more frequently in authoritarian families
    c. Conflicts sometimes arise over the choice of friends.
    d. Boys report more conflict with family members than girls.

_____ 5. Sex role is related to
    a. one's personal relationships
    b. one's work
    c. one's opinions
    d. all of the above

_____ 6. Which of the following did not view adolescence as a time of crisis and torment?
    a. Hall   **c.** Erikson
    b. Marcia   **d.** Bandura

_____ 7. Joan uses the "Golden Rule" as her guide in making moral judgments. She is considered to be in stage _____ of Kohlberg's design.
    a. one   **c.** four
    b. three   **d.** six

_____ 8. Which of the following tends not to describe early maturing boys?
    a. leaders in informal groups
    b. rebellious
    c. independent
    d. self-confident

_____ **9.** Max is androgynous according to the Bem scale. Which of the following would not describe him?
   a. flexible
   b. warm
   c. assertive
   d. unable to be playful

_____ **10.** All of the following statements about adolescence are true except
   a. occurrence of teenage suicide has grown
   b. troubled adolescents usually outgrow their problems
   c. adolescence offers unique challenges
   d. majority of adolescents adjust fairly quickly to emotional and social change

Directions: Place a + in the space at the left of each true statement. Place a 0 at the left of each false statement. (2 points each)

_____ **11.** All cultures define adolescence in precisely the same way.

_____ **12.** Belonging to a clique serves several important functions.

_____ **13.** Puberty marks the end of childhood.

_____ **14.** The adolescent deals with certain emotional feelings through rationalization.

_____ **15.** In authoritarian families, parents are the bosses.

_____ **16.** There are several different parenting styles.

_____ **17.** Asynchrony is a challenge that faces only adults.

_____ **18.** Bandura originated the concept of adolescence as a psychological stage.

_____ **19.** Research indicates that late maturing boys are at a disadvantage.

_____ **20.** A girl's first menstrual period usually occurs between the ages of 10 and 12.

_____ **21.** Erikson argues for the acceptance of androgynous roles.

_____ **22.** Formal operational thinking is found consistently among adolescents of various cultures.

_____ **23.** Erikson feels that building an identity is unique to adolescence.

_____ **24.** All psychologists agree that adolescents experience an identity crisis.

_____ **25.** Bandura is associated with the social learning theory of development.

Directions: In the space at the left, write the term or terms that best complete the statement. (2 points each)

_____ 26. _____ marks the biological end of childhood.

_____ 27. Bandura's approach is usually referred to as the _____ theory of development.

_____ 28. Adolescence is considered a(n) _____ stage between childhood and adulthood.

_____ 29. Margaret Mead's studies in _____ led her to believe that human development is a continuous process.

_____ 30. In _____ families, the parents are in control.

_____ 31. The adolescent fear of being disliked often leads to _____ , or acting in a way that copies or is similar to peers.

_____ 32. Robert Havighurst theorized that every _____ must master certain developmental tasks.

_____ 33. The major development task of adolescence is building a(n) _____ .

_____ 34. _____ rites are rites of passage from one age or status to another.

_____ 35. The anthropologist _____ found that in some cultures adolescence is a highly enjoyable time, unmarked by storm and stress.

Directions: Match each person or term in the left column with the best association. Write the letter of the association in the space provided. (2 points each)

_____ **36.** peer

a. ritual in which an individual is admitted into a new status

_____ **37.** menarche

b. classic anthropological studies

_____ **38.** rationalization

c. acting according to some specific authority

_____ **39.** Kohlberg

d. process by which an individual explains an unpleasant event in a way that preserves his or her self-esteem

_____ **40.** self-fulfilling prophecy

e. condition during which growth and maturation are uneven

_____ **41.** initiation rite

f. expectation that operates to bring about its own fulfillment

_____ **42.** asynchrony

g. according to Erikson, a time of storm and stress during which adolescents worry about who they are

_____ **43.** Mead

h. one who is in equal standing with another

_____ **44.** conformity

i. the first menstrual period

_____ **45.** identity crisis

j. contended that moral development occurs in stages

Directions: Answer the following questions on a separate sheet of paper. (5 points each)

46. Discuss the concept of identity for the adolescent.

47. Discuss the transition to adult thinking schemes.

CHAPTER 10 Test

Form A

ADULTHOOD AND OLD AGE

Directions: In the space at the left, write the letter of the choice that best completes the statement or answers the question. (2 points each)

_____ 1. John is statistically at his physical peak. He is most likely _____ years old.
    a. 30-35   **c.** 18-25
    b. 25-30   **d.** 15-18

_____ 2. Which is the order of the stages of dying as defined by Kübler-Ross?
    a. anger, denial, bargaining, depression, acceptance
    b. bargaining, anger, denial, acceptance, depression
    c. denial, anger, bargaining, depression, acceptance
    d. denial, bargaining, anger, depression, acceptance

_____ 3. As a person ages, the sensory apparatus requires
    a. less stimulation
    b. approximately the same stimulation
    c. greater stimulation
    d. less stimulation but prolonged amounts of it

_____ 4. Investigations of intelligence and aging have revealed all of the following except
    a. scores on performance tests decline
    b. scores on verbal tests remain relatively stable
    c. new information is acquired and vocabularies expanded
    d. new information is not well integrated due to inflexibility in thinking

_____ 5. What percent of the aged suffer from senility?
    a. five   **c.** fifteen
    b. ten   **d.** twenty

_____ 6. Robert believes that his function in life is to help younger generations by passing on his acquired wisdom in business. Erikson would label his psychosocial position as one of
    a. despair   **c.** generativity
    b. stagnation   **d.** ego integrity

_____ 7. Carol has just stopped ovulating. She is most likely between the ages of
    a. 30-35   **c.** 45-50
    b. 10-17   **d.** 55-60

_____ 8. George is at that stage of life where he is assessing his accomplishments and determining whether or not they have been satisfying. He is most likely in the age bracket of
    a. 35-40
    b. 40-45
    c. 45-50
    d. 55-60

_____ 9. Janice is struggling through the second stage of dying. This can best be described as a stage of
   a. anger
   b. denial
   c. acceptance
   d. bargaining

_____ 10. Joe is biologically at his sexual peak. Which of the following is most likely his age?
   a. 18
   b. 25
   c. 35
   d. 45

Directions: Place a + in the space at the left of each true statement. Place a 0 at the left of each false statement. (2 points each)

_____ 11. Thanatology is the study of death and dying.

_____ 12. The developmental tasks of both adolescence and adulthood involve bodily changes that require psychological adjustments. Such experiences can serve as a basis for improved communication between generations.

_____ 13. Part of the purpose of hospice care is to provide the patient as normal a life as possible.

_____ 14. Women reach their sexual peak later than men and the decline in their sexual responsiveness occurs later than in men.

_____ 15. Generativity versus stagnation is the main conflict in early adulthood.

_____ 16. Levinson based his theory solely on the study of males.

_____ 17. Despite social and economic change, women remain the ones who for the most part are responsible for housework and child care.

_____ 18. Crystallized intelligence can be described as the ability to use one's knowledge and learning in appropriate situations.

_____ 19. The process of physical decline tends to be gradual.

_____ 20. Sexual activity, according to Masters and Johnson, automatically declines with age.

_____ 21. One's basic character is relatively stable over the years.

_____ 22. Erikson calls the desire to pass wisdom to future generations ego-integrity.

_____ 23. The health of an older person is generally related to his or her health when younger.

_____ 24. The quality of health care for the elderly is the same as that for the general population.

_____ 25. A man reaches his sexual peak in his late twenties.

Directions: In the space at the left, write the term or terms that best complete the statement. (2 points each)

_____ 26. _____ felt that personality was set during childhood and adolescence and did not consider the later development of the individual.

_____ 27. A person's _____ begins to slow as he or she ages.

_____ 28. Levinson's research focus on _____ .

_____ 29. Erikson's term for "hanging on to the past" is _____ .

_____ 30. About _____ percent of the elderly are able to carry out normal activities.

_____ 31. The last stage of dying is called _____ .

_____ 32. A(n) _____ is a special place where the terminally ill can go to die.

_____ 33. When the patient is not aware of the terminal nature of his or her illness but the staff and family are, it is called _____ awareness.

_____ 34. The _____ test of intelligence takes into account verbal as well as performance categories.

_____ 35. Prejudice against the elderly is called _____ .

Directions: Match each person or term in the left column with the best association. Write the letter of the association in the space provided. (2 points each)

_____ 36. menopause

_____ 37. Kübler-Ross

_____ 38. stagnation

_____ 39. Wechsler

_____ 40. Levinson

_____ 41. dying

_____ 42. mid-life transition

_____ 43. ageism

_____ 44. late adulthood

_____ 45. Gray Panthers

a. support group

b. decremental model of aging

c. end of reproductive capability

d. generativity

e. hospice

f. intelligence test

g. mentor and protege

h. retirement, widowhood

i. theory of male development

j. 5 stages of dying

Directions: Answer the following questions. Use a separate sheet of paper if necessary. (5 points each)

46. Discuss Levinson's stages of adult male growth. Give examples.

_____

_____

_____

_____

_____

_____

_____

_____

_____

_____

47. Discuss the effects of societal attitudes toward the elderly on their own self-concept.

_____

_____

_____

_____

_____

_____

_____

_____

_____

_____

CHAPTER 10 Test

Form B

ADULTHOOD AND OLD AGE

Directions: In the space at the left, write the letter of the choice that best completes the statement or answers the question. (2 points each)

_____ 1. Levinson's study focused on
    a. adult males
    b. adolescents
    c. elderly females
    d. all of the above

_____ 2. Some of the developmental tasks that adults face include
    a. taking on civic responsibilities
    b. occupational choice and achievement
    c. finding leisure activities
    d. all of the above

_____ 3. Two of the most common health problems of middle age are
    a. obesity and diabetes
    b. heart disease and cancer
    c. ulcerative conditions and cerebral stroke
    d. heart disease and cerebral stroke

_____ 4. According to Erikson, a successful mid-life transition fosters a sense of
    a. generativity
    b. integrity
    c. consolidation
    d. resolution

_____ 5. The four most prevalent chronic diseases of the elderly are
    a. heart disease, hypertension, diabetes, arthritis
    b. cerebral stroke, hypertension, diabetes, arthritis
    c. cancer, heart disease, diabetes, arthritis
    d. cancer, hypertension, cerebral stroke, arthritis

_____ 6. Morris is in that minority of elderly citizens that suffer from senility. This encompasses about _____ percent of the elderly population.
    a. 40
    b. 30
    c. 20
    d. 10

_____ 7. Marty is in the stage Levinson called middle adulthood. Which age group is he most likely in?
    a. 65-70
    b. 45-60
    c. 35-40
    d. 25-30

_____ **8.** Doctors and nurses have openly discussed Barney's terminal condition with him. This is a state of
 a. closed awareness
 b. open awareness
 c. mutual pretense awareness
 d. suspected awareness

_____ **9.** Which of the following statements is true?
 a. Two-worker families are the exception in today's society.
 b. The empty-nest period is always a traumatic transition.
 c. Depression is most common among young adult males.
 d. Women are more likely to suffer from depression than men are.

_____ **10.** John is in that stage of adulthood where he faces the conflict between the need to explore and the need to establish a stable life style. He is in the age group of
 a. 22-28
 b. 30-35
 c. 35-40
 d. 40-45

Directions: Place a + in the space at the left of each true statement. Place a 0 at the left of each false statement. (2 points each)

_____ **11.** Menopause leads to a reduction in sexual drive.

_____ **12.** An individual's basic character is stable over the adult years.

_____ **13.** The adulthood years are a time when lifestyle may set the stage for health problems that may show up late in life.

_____ **14.** Scarf theorizes that many women experience depression largely because of the traditional feminine sex-role stereotype.

_____ **15.** Thanatology is the study of aging.

_____ **16.** Ageism is prejudice against the elderly.

_____ **17.** The empty-nest syndrome applies to men and women.

_____ **18.** The first stage of psychological adjustments to dying is denial.

_____ **19.** Menopause occurs between the ages of 50 and 60 for most women.

_____ **20.** Intellectual development reaches a peak in the mid-twenties.

_____ **21.** "Becoming one's own man" occurs between the ages of thirty-six and forty, according to Levinson's research.

_____ **22.** Rigidity is a response to aging rather than a lifelong habit.

_____ **23.** Sexual activity, according to Masters and Johnson, automatically declines with age.

_____ **24.** Women are generally responsible for a larger share of housework and child care than are men.

_____ **25.** Hospices provide support and valuable aid to their clients.

Directions: In the space at the left, write the term or terms that best complete the statement. (2 points each)

_____ **26.** The biological termination of ovulation is called _____ .

_____ **27.** Erikson used the term _____ to refer to an individual's desire to use his or her wisdom to help others.

_____ **28.** According to Levinson, the mid-life transition begins at about age _____ .

_____ **29.** Most of our attitudes about aging are based on the _____ model of aging.

_____ **30.** Levinson's data revealed that many men experience the age _____ crisis.

_____ **31.** _____ is the study of death and dying.

_____ **32.** The elderly generally need _____ sleep than younger people do.

_____ **33.** When the patient is aware of the terminal nature of his or her illness, it is called _____ awareness.

_____ **34.** Kübler-Ross identified _____ stages of psychological adjustment to death.

_____ **35.** _____ intelligence is the ability to solve abstract relational problems and generate new hypotheses.

Directions: Match each person or term in the left column with the best association. Write the letter of the association in the space provided. (2 points each)

_____ **36.** Scarf

_____ **37.** Alzheimer's

_____ **38.** thanatology

_____ **39.** males, aged 22-28

_____ **40.** males, aged 36-40

_____ **41.** cohort effect

_____ **42.** open awareness

_____ **43.** closed awareness

_____ **44.** suspected awareness

_____ **45.** empty nest

a. disease that affects cognitive functioning of elderly

b. BOOM phase

c. study of death and dying

d. idea that people from different age groups generally have different experiences

e. situation in which medical staff and family are aware of patient's terminal condition, but patient is not

f. situation in which patient suspects illness is terminal and endeavors to find out truth

g. novice in adult world

h. situation in which patient is aware that illness is terminal

i. *Unfinished Business*

j. event in women's lives when last child moves out of home

Directions: Answer the following questions on a separate sheet of paper. (5 points each)

46. Discuss Kübler-Ross's stages of psychological adjustment to terminal illness.

47. Discuss the physical, sexual, and health changes that occur with the process of aging.

Name _____ Date _____ Class _____

 **Test**   **Form A**

PERSONALITY THEORY

Directions: In the space at the left, write the letter of the choice that best completes the statement or answers the question. (2 points each)

_____ 1. According to Freud, the part of the psyche that stops a person from stealing is the
    a. ego
    b. superego
    c. id
    d. collective unconscious

_____ 2. Freud saw the _____ as operating in terms of the reality principle.
    a. ego
    b. id
    c. superego
    d. archetypes

_____ 3. According to Freud, basic sexual and aggressive drives reside in the
    a. ego
    b. superego
    c. collective unconscious
    d. id

_____ 4. Thinking that someone is angry at you when in reality you despise the person and cannot accept your feelings is called
    a. repression
    b. regression
    c. projection
    d. reaction formation

_____ 5. Marty gets angry at his wife when she isn't taking care of him. The real object of his anger is his mother. This defense mechanism is called
    a. projection
    b. displacement
    c. reaction formation
    d. repression

_____ 6. A three-year-old child who has been toilet trained starts wetting the bed after the birth of a sibling. This child is using the defense of
    a. projection
    b. repression
    c. displacement
    d. regression

_____ **7.** Mrs. Smith smothers her child with love, although unconsciously she is very angry at the child. She is displaying the defense mechanism of
  a. projection
  b. repression
  c. displacement
  d. reaction formation

_____ **8.** Jung's term for the part of the psyche similar to Freud's "unconscious" is
  a. id
  b. superego
  c. collective unconscious
  d. personal unconscious

_____ **9.** The term "inferiority complex" was introduced by
  a. Skinner   **c.** Adler
  b. Jung   **d.** Horney

_____ **10.** American psychology has been dominated by the study of
  a. trait theory
  b. human and animal learning
  c. psychoanalysis
  d. humanistic psychology

_____ **11.** Rewards and punishments are associated with
  a. psychoanalysis
  b. trait theory
  c. behavioral psychology
  d. humanistic psychology

_____ **12.** Maslow deliberately tried to establish an alternative to psychoanalysis and
  a. behaviorism
  b. trait theory
  c. neo-Freudian approaches
  d. humanistic psychology

_____ **13.** Betty is considered a self-actualizing individual. She most likely does not
  a. accept herself as she is
  b. perceive reality accurately
  c. feel herself free from emotional difficulties
  d. have a problem-centered style of adapting

_____ **14.** Which of the following does not describe the self-actualizing individual?
  a. spontaneous   **c.** sense of humor
  b. self-centered   **d.** values privacy

_____ **15.** _____ can be described as people who are thoughtful, passive, and quiet.
  a. Self-actualized individuals
  b. Archetypes
  c. Extraverts
  d. Introverts

Directions: Place a + in the space at the left of each true statement. Place a 0 at the left of each false statement. (2 points each)

_____ **16.** For Freud, the most powerful influences on our personality are things of which we are not conscious.

_____ **17.** The source of guilt is the superego.

_____ **18.** Unconscious forgetting is called displacement.

_____ **19.** Adler did not emphasize early child rearing patterns.

_____ **20.** Self-actualizers accept their environment more easily than the average person.

Directions: In the space at the left, write the term or terms that best complete the statement. (2 points each)

_____ **21.** _____ was the first modern psychologist to suggest the importance of unconscious motives.

_____ **22.** According to Freud, the reservoir of instinctual urges is the _____ .

_____ **23.** The personality process that is mostly conscious is the _____ .

_____ **24.** The source of the conscience and ideals is the _____ .

_____ **25.** When the ego unconsciously shifts the object of a wish, _____ has occurred.

_____ **26.** Unconscious forgetting is termed _____ .

_____ **27.** Replacing a feeling with its opposite is a(n) _____ .

_____ **28.** Seeing qualities in others that are really within ourselves is called _____ .

_____ **29.** Returning to a less mature pattern of behavior is _____ .

_____ **30.** Jung called the _____ the storehouse of instincts.

_____ **31.** Jung called inherited universal ideas _____ .

_____ **32.** Adler believed that the driving force in humans is the desire to overcome feelings of _____ .

_____ **33.** The whole of a person is termed the _____ by Rogers.

_____ **34.** Allport called the study of one person in detail the _____ approach.

_____ **35.** The psychologist _____ contended that, in a fully functioning individual, the organism and self are one.

Directions: Match each person in the left column with the best association. Write the letter of the association in the space provided. (2 points each)

_____ **36.** Freud

_____ **37.** Fromm

_____ **38.** Jung

_____ **39.** Adler

_____ **40.** Bandura

_____ **41.** Skinner

_____ **42.** Maslow

_____ **43.** Rogers

_____ **44.** Allport

_____ **45.** Eysenck

a. collective unconscious

b. contingencies of reinforcement

c. three dimensions of personality

d. *Letters From Jenny*

e. inferiority complex

f. loneliness of freedom

g. observational learning

h. psychoanalysis

i. self-actualization

j. unconditional positive regard

Directions: Answer the following questions on separate sheet of paper. (5 points each)

46. Discuss and illustrate the concept of defense mechanisms.

47. Discuss the importance of unconscious processes in the theories of Freud, Skinner, Rogers, and the trait theorists.

Test   **Form B**

PERSONALITY THEORY

Directions: In the space at the left, write the letter of the choice that best completes the statement or answers the question. (2 points each)

_____ **1.** According to Freud, the structure of personality includes all of the following except
    a. ego
    b. superego
    c. id
    d. libido

_____ **2.** Freud was the first modern psychologist to suggest that
    a. radical behaviorism works
    b. every personality has a large unconscious component
    c. the proper subject matter of psychology is observable behavior
    d. all of the above

_____ **3.** Ways by which the ego unconsciously protects itself against unpleasant circumstances are called
    a. conformity
    b. critical periods
    c. defense mechanisms
    d. reaction formations

_____ **4.** According to Carl Rogers, the two parts of every person are the
    a. superego and ego
    b. superego and id
    c. id and ego
    d. organism and self

_____ **5.** Skinner's approach to personality may best be characterized as
    a. introverted
    b. psychoanalytic
    c. displacement
    d. pragmatic

_____ **6.** Who of the following would not be considered a neo-Freudian?
    a. Maslow
    b. Fromm
    c. Horney
    d. Erikson

_____ **7.** Jung calls themes that reappear in myths and folklores
    a. regressions
    b. archetypes
    c. personal unconscious
    d. collective unconscious

        Understanding Psychology   **85**

_____ 8. Many of Allport's ideas about personality are similar to those of
        a. psychoanalysis
        b. behaviorism
        c. humanistic psychology
        d. Adlerian psychology

_____ 9. Which of the following is a Rogerian term?
        a. organism
        b. conditions of worth
        c. unconditional positive regard
        d. all of the above

_____ 10. Which of the following is not associated with Eysenck?
        a. extraversion
        b. introversion
        c. conditions of worth
        d. psychoticism

Directions: Place a + in the space at the left of each true statement. Place a 0 at the left of each false statement. (2 points each)

_____ 11. Behaviors that characterize individuals are called traits.

_____ 12. One type of defense mechanism is repression.

_____ 13. Seeing anger in others while being out of touch with your own anger might be an example of projection.

_____ 14. Freud was originally trained as a medical doctor.

_____ 15. Questions on how life can be improved are not in the domain of personality theorists.

_____ 16. Freud's theory emphasizes everyone's potential for growth.

_____ 17. For Freud, the death instincts were the most important part of his theory.

_____ 18. For Jung, universal memories are termed archetypes.

_____ 19. Adler felt a child should learn generosity from his or her mother.

_____ 20. Skinner is more concerned with prediction and control than with understanding.

_____ 21. The ego is more concerned with wants than with cans.

_____ 22. The behaviorists have been less successful with normal people than with severely disturbed individuals.

_____ 23. The greater the gap between self and organism the more defensive a person becomes.

_____ **24.** Some psychologists believe that a few basic traits are central for everyone.

_____ **25.** Self-actualizers tend to avoid solitude.

Directions: In the space at the left, write the term or terms that best complete the statement. (2 points each)

_____ **26.** _____ coined the term "inferiority complex."

_____ **27.** Psychologists who adhere to _____ theory hold that the proper subject matter of psychology is observable behavior.

_____ **28.** Skinner called the occurrence of a reward or punishment following a particular behavior _____ of reinforcement.

_____ **29.** Bandura contended that personality is acquired, in part, by _____ learning.

_____ **30.** Harry Stack Sullivan regarded personality as a function of a person's _____ .

_____ **31.** _____ based his cognitive theory on an analysis of ourselves and our environment.

_____ **32.** Dollard and Miller used _____ theory to analyze Freud's ideas.

_____ **33.** Humanistic psychology is founded on the belief that people strive for _____ .

_____ **34.** _____ based his personality studies on what he termed self-actualized people.

_____ **35.** Rogers's term for an individual whose organism and self coincide is _____ .

Directions: Match each person or term in the left column with the best association. Write the letter of the association in the space provided. (2 points each)

_____ **36.** id

_____ **37.** ego

_____ **38.** trait

_____ **39.** archetype

a. ascribing one's undesirable attitudes or feelings to others

b. redirecting impulses or desires to a substitute

c. a tendency to react in a certain way

d. according to Freud, the part of personality that is in touch with reality

_____ **40.** introvert

     e. reserved, withdrawn individual

_____ **41.** superego

     f. according to Freud, that part of the unconscious personality that contains needs, drives, and instincts

_____ **42.** regression

     g. return to earlier state of development

_____ **43.** displacement

     h. excluding a painful memory from conscious awareness

_____ **44.** repression

     i. a Jungian term that is defined as an inherited idea

_____ **45.** projection

     j. according to Freud, that part of personality that inhibits undesirable impulses

Directions: Answer the following questions on a separate sheet of paper. (5 points each)

46. Compare and contrast the behavioral and humanistic models of personality.

47. Using the theories described in this chapter, discuss pessimistic and optimistic tendencies in personality theory.

Test

PSYCHOLOGICAL TESTING

Form A

***

Directions: In the space at the left, write the letter of the choice that best completes the statement or answers the question. (2 points each)

_____ 1. It is found that a test designed to measure management ability is a very good predictor of how well an individual will function as a manager. This test is said to be
   a. objective
   b. reliable
   c. standard
   d. valid

_____ 2. Which of the following is not true of good study and test-taking habits?
   a. material to be memorized should be read more than once, spaced over several intervals
   b. test takers should not puzzle too long over difficult items, but answer the easier items first and come back later if time permits
   c. a high level of anxiety improves test performance
   d. test takers should arrive on time for the test and wear a watch

_____ 3. A college admissions test, designed to find out whether an individual would make a good architectural student based on the skills that person has, is an example of an _____ test.
   a. achievement
   b. aptitude
   c. intelligence
   d. interest

_____ 4. When an algebra teacher gives a test to her class to measure how much algebra her students have learned, she is giving an _____ test.
   a. interest
   b. aptitude
   c. intelligence
   d. achievement

_____ 5. Use of a driving simulator machine to measure driving ability is an example of a(n) _____ test.
   a. situational
   b. aptitude
   c. projective
   d. objective

_____ 6. Each half of a test is scored separately. The two scores are approximately equal. This is one indication that the test is reliable. We also conclude that
   a. the test was properly standardized
   b. the test was properly normed
   c. the test is valid
   d. none of the above

_____ 7. A test that is administered twice to the same person with very different results cannot be called
   a. valid
   b. standardized
   c. reliable
   d. objective

_____ 8. The Stanford-Binet test measures intelligence in terms of
   a. mental age
   b. manual dexterity
   c. reading ability
   d. verbal ability

_____ 9. An individual has a mental age of 10 and a chronological age of 50. Her IQ on the original Binet test would be
   a. 200
   b. 100
   c. 50
   d. 20

_____ 10. One way to build your confidence before taking a standardized test is to
   a. become familiar with the format of the test ahead of time
   b. find out how wrong answers will affect your score
   c. rest before taking the test
   d. all of the above

Directions: Place a + in the space at the left of each true statement. Place a 0 at the left of each false statement. (2 points each)

_____ 11. If a student takes the same test twice and receives the same score each time, the test is said to be valid.

_____ 12. There is no way to prepare yourself for taking college entrance exams.

_____ 13. In checking tests for reliability, psychologists are trying to prevent variables from influencing a person's score.

_____ 14. Questions on some intelligence tests give middle-class people an advantage.

_____ 15. A raw score can tell us where an individual stands in relation to others at his or her age and grade levels.

_____ 16. In preparing to take an exam, the ideal study habit is to study for one long period the night before the exam.

_____ 17. Norms are the same as standards of performance.

_____ 18. A highly reliable test will screen out all interferences, such as the unpleasantness of the environment in which the test is administered.

_____ 19. The first intelligence test was designed in the United States.

_____ **20.** In the original Binet test, a slow learner was one who has a mental age lower than his or her chronological age.

_____ **21.** In general, norms for intelligence tests are established so that most people score near 100.

_____ **22.** Examples of group-administered intelligence tests are the Army Alpha and Beta tests.

_____ **23.** A student who needs to study for a French exam, a Spanish exam, and a geometry exam should plan to study the two languages close together.

_____ **24.** Aptitude tests measure innate ability.

_____ **25.** The best-known interest test is the Rorschach test.

Directions: In the space at the left, write the term or terms that best complete the statement. (2 points each)

_____ **26.** A test's ability to yield the same result under a variety of different circumstances is referred to as _____ .

_____ **27.** A system for ranking test scores that indicates the percentage of scores lower and higher than a given score is the _____ system.

_____ **28.** According to the original Binet intelligence test, a slow learner was one who had a(n) _____ age that was less than his or her _____ age.

_____ **29.** The WAIS-R is an intelligence test used with _____ .

_____ **30.** An example of an aptitude test is the _____ .

_____ **31.** An example of an interest test is the _____ .

_____ **32.** The most widely used objective personality test is the _____ .

_____ **33.** The best known and most widely discussed projective measure of personality is the _____ .

_____ **34.** A test that measures performance in terms of emotional, attitudinal, and behavioral responses to "true life" settings is called a(n) _____ test.

_____ **35.** The purpose of a(n) _____ test is to determine an individual's preferences and attitudes.

Directions: Match each term in the left column with the best association. Write the letter of the association in the space provided. (2 points each)

_____	**36.** reliability	**a.** adaptive testing
_____	**37.** validity	**b.** adult IQ test
_____	**38.** Stanford-Binet	**c.** college admission test
_____	**39.** Army Alpha	**d.** group test
_____	**40.** SAT	**e.** interest test
_____	**41.** Küder Preference Record	**f.** IQ test
_____	**42.** MMPI-2	**g.** measures what it is supposed to measure
_____	**43.** TAT	**h.** objective personality test
_____	**44.** WAIS-R	**i.** projective test
_____	**45.** CAT	**j.** test-retest

Directions: Answer the following questions on a separate sheet of paper. (5 points each)

46. Discuss the basic characteristics of tests: reliability, validity, and norms.

47. Discuss ways of reducing your test-taking anxiety and improving your score on college entrance exams.

CHAPTER **12** **Test**   **Form B**

PSYCHOLOGICAL TESTING

Directions: In the space at the left, write the letter of the choice that best completes the statement or answers the question. (2 points each)

_____ **1.** A student finds out that she was ranked in the 85th percentile on her college entrance exams. This means that
   a. 85 percent of her answers were correct
   b. 85 percent of the students in the standardization group scored lower
   c. 85 percent of the students in the standardization group scored higher
   d. the test is valid

_____ **2.** If two teachers grade the same test paper and assign the same score to the paper, the test is said to be
   a. reliable
   b. valid
   c. objective
   d. standard

_____ **3.** In taking any test, it is important to
   a. read the instructions carefully
   b. allot your time wisely
   c. believe in yourself and not panic
   d. all of the above

_____ **4.** High school guidance counselors often give students tests designed to predict how successful and happy they might be in particular careers. This type of test is called an
   a. interest test
   b. aptitude test
   c. intelligence test
   d. achievement test

_____ **5.** The fairness and usefulness of a test depend on
   a. its reliability
   b. its validity
   c. the way its norms were established
   d. all of the above

_____ **6.** In order to interpret test scores meaningfully, the test must be given to
   a. a random sample of the population
   b. a large and well-defined group of people
   c. a small and well-defined group of peoples
   d. none of the above

_____ **7.** The best way to compensate for differences in background and age is to compare test results from people of the same age who have similar backgrounds to get a
   a. valid result

b. standardized result
c. reliable result
d. purposeful result

_____ 8. Dividing mental age by chronological age and multiplying the result by 100 is called the
   a. Wechsler result
   b. Binet intelligence
   c. intelligence quotient
   d. Stanford intelligence

_____ 9. In comparison to the Stanford-Binet test, the Wechsler tests put more emphasis on
   a. words and verbal abilities
   b. inherited genetic traits
   c. performance tasks
   d. vocational interests

_____ 10. The TAT requires that the test taker respond to
   a. a questionnaire
   b. a set of inkblots
   c. a set of scenes depicted on cards
   d. pictures of animals

Directions: Place a + in the space at the left of each true statement. Place a 0 at the left of each false statement. (2 points each)

_____ 11. Grading on a curve is similar to using a percentile system.

_____ 12. Tests designed to determine a person's preferences, attitudes, and interests are called situational tests.

_____ 13. A danger of testing is that people tend to see test scores as ends in themselves.

_____ 14. In checking tests for reliability, psychologists are trying to prevent chance factors from influencing a person's score.

_____ 15. Most intelligence tests include questions concerning general knowledge or information.

_____ 16. If two teachers score the same test paper and assign almost identical grades to the paper, the test is said to be reliable.

_____ 17. The norming of a test involves the careful selection of test questions that are appropriate for some particular group.

_____ 18. Determining the validity of a test is more complex than assessing its reliability.

_____ 19. The first intelligence test was designed to identify gifted children so they could be placed in special, advanced classes.

_____ **20.** The Stanford-Binet intelligence test is administered on an individual basis.

_____ **21.** The Army Alpha and the Stanford-Binet are both very time-consuming and costly to administer.

_____ **22.** IQ scores are quite accurate in predicting success in school.

_____ **23.** It is always best to guess on test questions rather than not answer.

_____ **24.** All clinical tests are projective.

_____ **25.** Projective tests have a flaw in that the interpretation of responses is left open to the biases of the examiner.

Directions: In the space at the left, write the term or terms that best complete the statement. (2 points each)

_____ **26.** The count of the number of items on a test to which an individual has provided the correct answer is called his or her _____ score.

_____ **27.** The development of standards of comparison for test results by giving the test to large, well-defined groups of people is called _____ .

_____ **28.** To administer an intelligence test, the examiner must use _____ instructions.

_____ **29.** In general, the norms for intelligence tests are established in such a way that most people score _____ .

_____ **30.** Tests that encourage respondents to respond freely, giving their own interpretations of various test stimuli are called _____ tests.

_____ **31.** An example of an aptitude test is the _____ .

_____ **32.** is the ability of a test to measure what it is supposed to measure.

_____ **33.** The Army _____ test measures performance.

_____ **34.** The Army _____ test measures verbal skills.

_____ **35.** The Netherlands study analyzed the relation between _____ and IQ.

Directions: Match each person or term in the left column with the best association. Write the letter of the association in the space provided. (2 points each)

_____ 36. norms

_____ 37. split-half

_____ 38. inter-scorer

_____ 39. Murray

_____ 40. Gardner

_____ 41. Sternberg

_____ 42. culture-fair

_____ 43. Rorschach

_____ 44. mental age

_____ 45. chronological age

a. a test's ability to produce similar scores if the test is administered by different examiners

b. an individual's physical age

c. developed the TAT

d. a test without bias

e. standards of test performance

f. a test's ability to produce similar scores if parts or sections of the test are compared

g. 7 types of intelligence

h. typical intelligence level for people at a given age

i. test consisting of ink blots of indefinite shape

j. three-part theory of intelligence

Directions: Answer the following questions on a separate sheet of paper. (5 points each)

46. Describe Freud's psychoanalytic theory.

47. Discuss the major aspects of humanistic theories of personality.

CHAPTER 13 Test

STRESS AND HEALTH

Form A

Directions: In the space at the left, write the letter of the choice that best completes the statement or answers the question. (2 points each)

_____ 1. The mobilization for "fight or flight" occurs during the _____ stage.
   a. action
   b. resistance
   c. alarm
   d. internal

_____ 2. According to Holmes and Rahe, which of the following leads to the most stress?
   a. marital separation
   b. personal injury or illness
   c. death of a friend
   d. death of a spouse

_____ 3. George is considered a Type A person. He
   a. is prone to heart attacks in his thirties and forties
   b. is prone to heart attacks in his seventies
   c. has a low level of adrenalin
   d. is not competitive

_____ 4. After waiting all semester, John finally makes a date with a girl he has wanted to ask out for some time. Afterwards he realize that he unthinkingly made the date for the night before his final exam in physics, an exam he wanted to do well in. John is faced with
   a. an approach-approach conflict
   b. an avoidance-avoidance conflict
   c. an approach-avoidance conflict
   d. none of the above

_____ 5. The most widely abused drug today is
   a. marijuana   **c.** alcohol
   b. PCP   **d.** tobacco

_____ 6. Toby, a young boy, wants to pet a friend's dog, but is afraid that he will be nipped at by the dog. This is a(n) _____ conflict.
   a. avoidance-avoidance
   b. approach-avoidance
   c. approach-approach
   d. double approach-avoidance

_____ 7. According to Holmes and Rahe, which of the following produces the most stress?
   a. divorce
   b. death of a family member
   c. personal illness
   d. marriage

_____ **8.** Being barraged by more inputs than one can handle is called
   a. stimulus overload
   b. role conflict
   c. eustress
   d. approach-avoidance conflict

_____ **9.** Which of the following does not characterize Type A people?
   a. irritability
   b. free-floating hostility
   c. toleration for delay
   d. struggle

_____ **10.** Joey, watching gruesome films of torture, protects himself from feeling stress by blocking out the feelings associated with the scenes. This is an example of the coping strategy called
   a. intellectualization
   b. progressive relaxation
   c. cognitive awareness
   d. repression

Directions: Place a + in the space at the left of each true statement. Place a 0 at the left of each false statement. (2 points each)

_____ **11.** A stressor is a stress-providing event or situation.

_____ **12.** Stress does not produce long-term problems.

_____ **13.** Stress is an avoidable part of life.

_____ **14.** People who experience great amounts of stress are more likely to become physically ill.

_____ **15.** Type A people often have anger that has no real object or focus.

_____ **16.** The person with the lowest level of stress in his or her life is most likely to be the happiest.

_____ **17.** The approach-avoidance conflict is the most common conflict situation.

_____ **18.** According to Holmes and Rahe, divorce is the most stressful situation.

_____ **19.** Role conflict can be a source of on-the-job stress.

_____ **20.** Frustration is particularly stressful when caused by expected circumstances.

_____ **21.** The effects of crowding, according to Freedman, are dependent on the situation.

_____ **22.** According to Selye, the pupils dilate during the alarm state of stress.

_____ **23.** When a stressor involves a real danger it is called anxiety.

_____ **24.** Physical disorders are more likely when we do not have control over stressors.

_____ **25.** Social support can help reduce the likelihood of stress-related disease.

Directions: In the space at the left, write the term or terms that best complete the statement. (2 points each)

_____ **26.** Positive stress is often called _____ .

_____ **27.** Negative stress is often called _____ .

_____ **28.** Selye identified a total of _____ stages in the body's stress reaction.

_____ **29.** The Type _____ person is in a chronic state of stress.

_____ **30.** The "fight or flight" reaction occurs during the _____ stage.

_____ **31.** People who are not Type A tend not to have heart attacks before they are _____ years old.

_____ **32.** The most common conflict situation is a(n) _____ conflict.

_____ **33.** Most people spend more time at _____ than in any other activity.

_____ **34.** A person described as a(n) _____ tends to put the best face on any set of events.

_____ **35.** A(n) _____ tends to see the dark side of a situation.

Directions: Match each person, team, or term in the left column with the best association. Write the letter of the association in the space provided. (2 points each)

_____ **36.** stressor

_____ **37.** stress reaction

_____ **38.** meditation

_____ **39.** biofeedback

a. coping mechanism in which a situation is analyzed from an emotionally detached view

b. body's response to a stressor

c. conflict in which an individual must choose between two unattractive alternatives

d. process of focusing attention with goal of clearing mind and creating inner peace

_____ **40.** intellectualization

e. condition in which an individual suffers from a situation so severely that he or she believes that any effort to cope will fail

_____ **41.** learned helplessness

f. conflict in which the choice is between two attractive alternatives

_____ **42.** cognitive appraisal

g. conflict in which an individual wants to do something but fears it at the same time

_____ **43.** approach-avoidance

h. interpretation of an event that helps to determine its stress impact

_____ **44.** approach-approach

i. stress-producing event or situation

_____ **45.** avoidance-avoidance

j. process of learning to control bodily states with the help of machines

Directions: Answer the following questions on a separate sheet of paper. (5 points each)

46. Discuss Holmes and Rahe's findings on the nature of stressful events.

47. Discuss the short- and long-term psychological reactions to stress.

CHAPTER 13 Test

Form B

STRESS AND HEALTH

Directions: In the space at the left, write the letter of the choice that best completes the statement or answers the question. (2 points each)

_____ 1. The sequence of the stress response syndrome is
   a. alarm, resistance, exhaustion
   b. alarm, exhaustion, resistance
   c. exhaustion, alarm, resistance
   d. resistance, alarm, exhaustion

_____ 2. Eustress is a term that means
   a. social support   **c.** stress reaction
   b. positive stress   **d.** negative stress

_____ 3. A worker may suffer stress reactions as a result of
   a. assuming responsibility for other people
   b. work overload
   c. work underload
   d. all of the above

_____ 4. During the alarm stage of stress, a person would generally experience
   a. contraction of the pupils
   b. decreased activity of the adrenal glands
   c. quickening of the heartbeat and breathing
   d. all of the above

_____ 5. The impact of stress can be influenced by
   a. denial
   b. cognitive preparation
   c. intellectualization
   d. all of the above

_____ 6. George has been accepted by two colleges, both of which equally impress him. The stress situation he is in is called a(n) _____ conflict.
   a. approach-avoidance
   b. avoidance-avoidance
   c. approach-approach
   d. double approach-avoidance

_____ 7. Which of the following occupational stressors is not grouped under the category "the nature of the job"?
   a. work underload
   b. work overload
   c. working conditions
   d. responsibility for other people

_____ 8. Which of the following is not considered a short-term psychological reaction to stress?
   a. anger   **c.** fatigue
   b. fear   **d.** anxiety

_____ 9. According to Rahe and Arthur, the order of stress-related disease is _____ .
   a. perception, psychological response, protective behavior, physiological response, signs of illness, frank disease
   b. perception, psychological response, physiological response, protective behavior, signs of illness, frank disease
   c. signs of illness, physiological response, psychological response, perception, protective behavior, frank disease
   d. signs of illness, frank disease, protective behavior, perception, physiological response, psychological response

_____ 10. The _____ person is more vulnerable to stress.
   a. Type B   **c.** elderly
   b. Type A   **d.** none of the above

Directions: Place a + in the space at the left of each true statement. Place a 0 at the left of each false statement. (2 points each)

_____ 11. The Holmes-Rahe scale studies meditation techniques.

_____ 12. Frustration does not cause stress.

_____ 13. Noise is considered an environmental stressor.

_____ 14. A Type B person is in a chronic state of stress.

_____ 15. During the resistance stage of stress, the physical changes that occurred during the alarm stage continue.

_____ 16. An approach-approach conflict generally produces a great deal of stress.

_____ 17. In an approach-approach conflict, an individual must choose between two unattractive alternatives.

_____ 18. Work can be a prime source of stress.

_____ 19. According to Holmes and Rahe, divorce is the most stressful situation.

_____ 20. A common reaction to a sudden and powerful stressor is anxiety.

_____ 21. Milgram sees urban living as "stimulus underload."

_____ 22. During the exhaustion stage, the adrenal glands increase the supply of adrenalin.

_____ 23. Fear is a common reaction when a stressor involves actual danger.

_____ **24.** Alcohol is a stimulant.

_____ **25.** Jacobson developed the relaxation technique of meditation.

Directions: In the space at the left, write the term or terms that best complete the statement. (2 points each)

_____ **26.** Selye identified _____ stages of the body's response to stress.

_____ **27.** When danger threatens, people mobilize for "_____."

_____ **28.** Research indicates that _____ may be involved in the onset of diseases.

_____ **29.** _____ causes rapid heartbeat and breathing.

_____ **30.** Holmes and Rahe found that the _____ was the highest ranked stressful situation.

_____ **31.** The coping mechanism in which the individual decides the event is not really a stressor is called _____ .

_____ **32.** The conflict situation where only one goal is involved is a(n) _____ conflict.

_____ **33.** When progress toward a goal is blocked, the feeling of _____ arises.

_____ **34.** Stress reactions may be physical, behavioral, or psychological since we are _____ organisms.

_____ **35.** The coping strategy in which the individual mentally rehearses possible outcomes is called _____ preparation.

Directions: Match each person or term in the left column with the best association. Write the letter of the association in the space provided. (2 points each)

_____ **36.** adrenal glands

_____ **37.** alcohol

_____ **38.** anxiety

_____ **39.** eustress

_____ **40.** frustration

_____ **41.** Holmes and Rahe

_____ **42.** Type C

_____ **43.** Selye

_____ **44.** Type A person

_____ **45.** urban life

a. prone to coronary disease

b. positive stress

c. feeling of imminent, unclear threat

d. stages of stress

e. cancer-prone behavior patterns

f. Social Readjustment Rating Scale

g. stimulus overload

h. source of stress

i. extra energy

j. depressant

Directions: Answer the following questions on a separate sheet of paper. (5 points each)

46. Discuss psychological and behavioral stress-coping strategies.

47. Discuss the relationship between stress and disease.

Test Form A

ADJUSTMENT IN SOCIETY

Directions: In the space at the left, write the letter of the choice that best completes the statement or answers the question. (2 points each)

_____ 1. Rubin's research indicates that all of the following except _____ is not an element of romantic love.
   a. intimacy
   b. self-sacrifice
   c. need
   d. desire to give

_____ 2. During the _____ stage, married couples adjust to their children leaving home.
   a. conflict-habituated
   b. empty-nest
   c. children's adolescence
   d. homogamy

_____ 3. As individuals grow, they gain a sense of _____ , the ability to take care of themselves.
   a. adjustment
   b. endogamy
   c. autonomy
   d. none of the above

_____ 4. Conflict-ridden relationships are less likely to occur in families where the parents are
   a. authoritarian
   b. permissive
   c. democratic
   d. divorced

_____ 5. The tendency to marry someone who has similar attitudes is called
   a. passive-congenial
   b. conflict-habituated
   c. autonomy
   d. homogamy

_____ 6. Trying to combine old with new is a method of coping with change called
   a. total pursuit
   b. self-sacrifice
   c. resynthesis
   d. conflict-habituated

_____ 7. Which of the following is not a basic factor in a healthy adjustment to marriage?
   a. compatible needs
   b. political beliefs
   c. a partner's self-image coincides with the other's image of the partner
   d. agreement on respective roles

_____ 8. "You're acting just like a baby" is an example of the blaming technique called _____ , which leads to escalating conflict rather than to resolution.
   a. psychoanalyzing
   b. teaching
   c. shaming
   d. judging

_____ 9. Which of the following characterizes "resynthesis"?
   a. avoidance of situations leading to doubt
   b. emotional detachment
   c. redoubling of efforts in an area one has initially chosen
   d. keeping one's options open

_____ 10. Which of the following was not a finding of Rubin's research on love?
   a. couples scoring high on the love scale stared more into each other's eyes
   b. people scoring high on the love scale sacrificed their comfort for that of their partners
   c. women shared intimacies with friends of the same sex more than men did
   d. most couples were equal on the love scale

Directions: Place a + in the space at the left of each true statement. Place a 0 at the left of each false statement. (2 points each)

_____ 11. Hatfield distinguished between passionate love and compassionate love.

_____ 12. Madison found developmental friendships more important for students than professorial teaching.

_____ 13. Separation shock is the term applied to students going off to college.

_____ 14. Children adjust more easily to divorce than their parents.

_____ 15. Divorced couples may feel "separation shock."

_____ 16. Adjustment is a basically passive process of accepting the environment.

_____ 17. The well-adjusted person has managed to avoid all stress in life.

_____ 18. Peter Madison studied the effects of stress on working-class families.

_____ 19. Going to college often stimulates change.

_____ 20. Financial reward is an important element of job satisfaction.

_____ 21. Adjusting to divorce is generally more difficult for adults than for children.

_____ 22. The chance for conflict escalation is greatest in democratic families since everyone has something to say.

_____ 23. Madison found that student culture has a greater impact on students than do professors.

_____ **24.** Most people keep the same career throughout their lifetime.

_____ **25.** Adjustment is an active process.

Directions: In the space at the left, write the term or terms that best complete the statement. (2 points each)

_____ **26.** Adjustment is the process of adapting to as well as actively _____ one's environment.

_____ **27.** _____ has been defined as that state in which the happiness of another person is essential to our own.

_____ **28.** Sternberg theorizes that love consists of intimacy, passion, and _____ .

_____ **29.** According to the text, without _____ , caring is just charity or kindness.

_____ **30.** In many ways adjustment to _____ is like adjustment to death.

_____ **31.** Because their developmental stage already involves the breaking of family ties, _____ experience special problems as a result of parental divorce.

_____ **32.** The fact that adolescents and their parents have differing views on many issues has been labeled the _____ .

_____ **33.** _____ parents enforce only the guidelines their children let them enforce.

_____ **34.** Growing up involves gaining a sense of _____ , the ability to take care of one's self.

_____ **35.** One major source of work satisfaction is _____ , the help, supplies, and equipment to do the job well.

Directions: Match each term in the left column with the best association. Write the letter of the association in the space provided. (2 points each)

_____ **36.** romantic love

_____ **37.** developmental

_____ **38.** resynthesis

_____ **39.** democratic parents

_____ **40.** homogamy

_____ **41.** career

_____ **42.** liking

_____ **43.** authoritarian parents

_____ **44.** children period

_____ **45.** sex

a. based on respect and similarity

b. foster open communication

c. integrating old and new ideas and feelings

d. vocation

e. brings new responsibilities to parents

f. type of relationship in which friends force one another to examine assumptions

g. marrying someone like oneself

h. need, desire to give, intimacy

i. rely on power

j. source of parent-adolescent conflict

Directions: Answer the following questions on a separate sheet of paper. (5 points each)

46. Discuss Rubin's findings on liking and loving.

47. Discuss adjustments to college life as a source of change and how best to cope with that change.

CHAPTER 14 Test

Form B

ADJUSTMENT IN SOCIETY

Directions: In the space at the left, write the letter of the choice that best completes the statement or answers the question. (2 points each)

_____ 1. Rubin found that
   a. men were more romantic than women
   b. women were more romantic than men
   c. the sexes were equally romantic
   d. none of the above

_____ 2. Which of the following is not likely to lead to a successful marriage?
   a. similar economic backgrounds
   b. shared religion
   c. love at first sight
   d. same level of education

_____ 3. Sternberg contends that love consists of
   a. intimacy
   b. passion
   c. commitment
   d. all of the above

_____ 4. A well-adjusted person has learned
   a. how to avoid stress
   b. how to deal with frustrations
   c. how to withdraw from relationships that have conflicts
   d. all of the above

_____ 5. A person on her first full-time job usually experiences
   a. a need to compromise
   b. an initial "come down"
   c. tension
   d. all of the above

_____ 6. Which of the following statements is not true?
   a. more and more children have to cope with parents divorcing
   b. children of divorce exhibit limited reaction
   c. most children eventually come to terms with divorce
   d. adjustment is easier when parents take special care to explain the divorce

_____ 7. Couples surveyed identified _____ as the main reason for a successful marriage.
   a. we do everything together
   b. marriage is a long-term commitment
   c. we are involved in many social activities
   d. my spouse is my best friend

_____ 8. Which of the following is not true about the process of growing up?
   a. it begins before the individual leaves home
   b. it involves a physical, but not emotional, separation
   c. it involves gaining a sense of autonomy
   d. it involves developing a value system

_____ 9. Which of the following variables is irrelevant to a successful marriage?
   a. economic backgrounds
   b. intensity of early attachment to each other
   c. views on religion
   d. nature of parental marriages

_____ 10. In the course of his research Madison found that
   a. fewer people should change careers
   b. comparable worth is a worthy goal
   c. many students approach college with unrealistic expectations
   d. liking and loving share many attributes

Directions: Place a + in the space at the left of each true statement. Place a 0 at the left of each false statement. (2 points each)

_____ 11. Rubin showed that lovers sacrifice their comfort for that of their partners.

_____ 12. The actual tasks of a person's first job may be unexpected and disappointing.

_____ 13. Madison argued that college students should not strive for autonomy.

_____ 14. Adolescents typically feel a desire for total independence from their parents.

_____ 15. Among couples Rubin found that men and women score equally on the love scale.

_____ 16. Homogamy is the tendency to marry someone based on physical proximity.

_____ 17. Loving, according to Rubin, is based on respect and a perceived similarity with another person.

_____ 18. Sternberg noted that there are six components of love.

_____ 19. Generally, a period of mourning follows a divorce.

_____ 20. Adjusting to divorce is generally tranquil for children.

_____ 21. According to Rubin, need or attachment is one of the components of romantic love.

_____ 22. As family conflict escalates, many parents and children resort to counterproductive tactics.

_____ 23. There is a growing trend to settle in one career for a lifetime.

_____ **24.** Statistics show that people who are most satisfied with their work do the best job.

_____ **25.** People in love share a basic intimacy.

Directions: In the space at the left, write the term or terms that best complete the statement. (2 points each)

_____ **26.** Hatfield identified two common types of love: passionate and _____ .

_____ **27.** Rubin identified three major components of romantic love: need, _____ , and intimacy.

_____ **28.** Endogamy is the tendency to marry someone who is from the same _____ .

_____ **29.** Homogamy is the tendency to marry someone who has similar _____ .

_____ **30.** _____ shock tends to be the greatest for those individuals who saw divorce as liberation and did not anticipate difficulties.

_____ **31.** The _____ period of marriage generally means many adjustments for the new mother and father.

_____ **32.** Commenting on a person's possible psychological reasons for an action is using the blaming technique of _____ .

_____ **33.** "You're being selfish" is an example of a blaming tactic called _____ .

_____ **34.** "Don't you feel like a baby" is an example of a blaming tactic called _____ .

_____ **35.** _____ is based primarily on respect for another person.

Directions: Match each person or term in the left column with the best association. Write the letter of the association in the space provided. (2 points each)

_____ 36. Satir

    a. tendency to marry someone from same social group

_____ 37. Sternberg

    b. *Peoplemaking*

_____ 38. Rubin

    c. ability to take care of oneself

_____ 39. autonomy

    d. period representing shedding responsibilities and roles in family of origin and assuming new and different roles

_____ 40. endogamy

    e. research on coping with college life

_____ 41. Madison

    f. state characterized by intensity and sensuality

_____ 42. companionate love

    g. triangular theory of love

_____ 43. passionate love

    h. one of the effects of divorce

_____ 44. newlywed

    i. state characterized by friendship and mutual trust

_____ 45. separation shock

    j. research on liking and loving

Directions: Answer the following questions on a separate sheet of paper. (5 points each)

46. Discuss and give examples of a healthy adjustment to marriage.

47. Discuss the stressful situation of divorce and its effects on both the adults and the children involved.

Form A

ABNORMAL BEHAVIOR

Directions: In the space at the left, write the letter of the choice that best completes the statement or answers the question. (2 points each)

_____ 1. Insanity, a legal term, holds that
      a. a person is insane if he or she doesn't know the difference between right and wrong
      b. a person is not insane as long as he or she does not commit a crime
      c. only a judge can decide whether someone is insane or not
      d. a person is insane if diagnosed as having one of the more serious disorders

_____ 2. Thomas Szasz contends that people whom we label mentally ill
      a. are schizophrenic
      b. have a generalized anxiety disorder
      c. are not ill at all
      d. have psychosomatic problems

_____ 3. When a person feels very anxious and cannot stop thinking about something even though it is unpleasant, he or she suffers from
      a. a compulsion
      b. an obsession
      c. depression
      d. rigidity

_____ 4. A dissociative reaction occurs when a person
      a. changes careers
      b. gives up a lifelong friend or loses a spouse
      c. suffers from a loss of identity or memory
      d. develops an illness with no physical basis

_____ 5. Women are _____ as men to suffer from depression.
      a. as likely
      b. twice as likely
      c. half as likely
      d. none of the above

_____ 6. Well-adjusted people are considered normal. This means that
      a. they conform to all of society's rules
      b. they are never unhappy
      c. can get along in the world physically, emotionally, and socially
      d. anyone who feels lonely is maladjusted

_____ 7. Self-actualizing people
      a. do what is best for themselves regardless of how their acts affect others
      b. are always easy to get along with
      c. are trying to express their individuality and maximize their potential
      d. form the majority of the population

_____ 8. Defining abnormality as deviation from normality
   a. is accepted under the DSM classification system
   b. has serious limitations
   c. is accepted by clinical psychologists
   d. none of the above

_____ 9. Somatoform disorders are characterized by
   a. physical symptoms that have no apparent physical causes
   b. uncontrollable laughter
   c. acute indigestion
   d. constant crying

_____ 10. An extreme fear of crowds is called
   a. monophobia
   b. claustrophobia
   c. acrophobia
   d. agoraphobia

Directions: Place a + in the space at the left of each true statement. Place a 0 at the left of each false statement. (2 points each)

_____ 11. The terms "sane" and "insane" are psychological distinctions often used by psychologists.

_____ 12. People with anxiety-based disorders live in a fantasy world.

_____ 13. A phobia may be a way of coping with anxiety.

_____ 14. Schizophrenia is characterized by confused, disordered thoughts and perceptions.

_____ 15. Alcohol is a depressant.

_____ 16. Psychologists have a list of actions and feelings that are abnormal as opposed to normal.

_____ 17. Conformity is always a sign of sound mental health.

_____ 18. The causes and symptoms of psychological disturbances are not always clear.

_____ 19. People with anxiety-based disorders tend to have unrealistic self-images.

_____ 20. A person with an anxiety-based or mild disorder has an average amount of anxiety.

_____ 21. Freud's first cases were hysterics.

_____ 22. More women than men succeed in committing suicide.

_____ 23. Autism is a form of schizophrenia and is most often observed in the elderly.

_____ **24.** A person with a manic-type reaction exhibits high activity and elation.

_____ **25.** Most cases of schizophrenia result from brain damage.

Directions: In the space at the left, write the term or terms that best complete the statement. (2 points each)

_____ **26.** The view that whatever most people do is normal is the _____ approach to mental illness.

_____ **27.** One definition of abnormality uses the criterion of failure to _____ .

_____ **28.** Severe anxiety focused on an object or situation is called a(n) _____ .

_____ **29.** The repetition of irrational actions is called a(n) _____ .

_____ **30.** When emotional problems produce real physical damage it's called a(n) _____ .

_____ **31.** Multiple personality is a type of _____ reaction.

_____ **32.** _____ involves disordered and confused thoughts and perceptions.

_____ **33.** The form of schizophrenia characterized by long periods of motionless is called _____ .

_____ **34.** _____ theory is an explanation of schizophrenia in communication terms.

_____ **35.** The most serious drug problem in this country is _____ .

Directions: Match each person or term in the left column with the best association. Write the letter of the association in the space provided. (2 points each)

_____ **36.** sane

a. amnesia and active flight

_____ **37.** Szasz

b. physical adaptation to a drug

_____ **38.** tolerance

c. body motionless for long periods

_____ **39.** phobia

d. childhood disorder like schizophrenia

_____ **40.** hypochondriasis

e. delusions and hallucinations

_____ **41.** fugue

f. elation and confusion

_____ **42.** autism

g. imaginary ailments

_____ **43.** schizophrenia

h. irrational fear

_____ **44.** catatonic type

i. legal term

_____ **45.** manic-type reaction

j. problems in living

Directions: Answer the following questions on a separate sheet of paper. (5 points each)

46. Is mental illness a myth? Discuss.

47. Discuss ways to distinguish abnormal from normal behavior.

CHAPTER 15 Test

Form B

ABNORMAL BEHAVIOR

Directions: In the space at the left, write the letter of the choice that best completes the statement or answers the question. (2 points each)

_____ 1. The advantage of the DSM system of classifying mental illness is that
   a. it is easy to use
   b. it allows for multiple diagnoses
   c. patients can diagnose their own illnesses
   d. it is especially accurate in diagnosing childhood schizophrenia

_____ 2. A phobia is characterized by
   a. constant unhappiness
   b. feeling euphoric for no apparent reason
   c. a limited attention span
   d. a persistent fear of a particular object or situation

_____ 3. Transforming emotional difficulties into the loss of a physiological function is known as
   a. fugue
   b. an obsession
   c. a dissociative reaction
   d. a conversion reaction

_____ 4. Guilt and the need for self-punishment are often associated with
   a. manic behavior
   b. fugue
   c. amnesia
   d. depression

_____ 5. A person with a bipolar disorder experiences alternating periods of
   a. a mild sadness and severe guilt
   b. frantic action and deep despair
   c. a wild fantasy life and sadness
   d. amnesia and despair

_____ 6. Abnormality can be defined as deviating from average behavior. This approach
   a. is an excellent method for diagnosing insanity
   b. has serious limitations
   c. is best used in small towns
   d. is more effective for diagnosing abnormality in men than in women

_____ 7. Which of the following is a clear sign of abnormality?
   a. a person's problem disrupts his or her everyday life
   b. a person dresses differently from the current fashion
   c. a person loses his or her job
   d. a person suddenly adopts a new religion

_____ 8. _____ is characterized by a misinterpretation of normal aches and pains.
   a. Hypochondriasis
   b. Multiple personality
   c. Psychogenic amnesia
   d. Phobia

_____ 9. Individuals with paranoid-type schizophrenia believe that
   a. no one else exists
   b. doctors are the source of their distress
   c. others are plotting against them
   d. none of the above

_____ 10. Which of the following is not a possible cause of schizophrenia?
   a. hereditary factors
   b. biochemical factors
   c. having only one parent
   d. double binds in childhood

Directions: Place a + in the space at the left of each true statement. Place a 0 at the left of each false statement. (2 points each)

_____ 11. A patient may fit into several diagnostic categories.

_____ 12. Dr. Thomas Szasz believes that people who are called "mentally ill" are not sick, but have "problems in living."

_____ 13. A severe anxiety concerning high places is called acrophobia.

_____ 14. Obsessions and compulsions occur only in neurotic people.

_____ 15. A sociopath is unlikely to feel any guilt.

_____ 16. A person who is different from what other people in his or her town consider normal is probably mentally disturbed.

_____ 17. All definitions of abnormality are highly reliable and valid.

_____ 18. Because of the way mental illnesses are classified, two psychiatrists will always agree on the nature of a person's problem.

_____ 19. People with anxiety-based disorders often feel unworthy or inferior to those around them.

_____ 20. Conversion reactions are frequent problems in present-day psychological practice.

_____ 21. Many depressives think about suicide.

_____ 22. Suicide is most common among the elderly.

_____ 23. "Word salad" is often observed in schizophrenics.

_____ **24.** An obsession is a fear of a situation that is out of proportion to the real dangers involved.

_____ **25.** Heredity may play a part in determining whether or not a person will become mentally ill.

Directions: In the space at the left, write the term or terms that best complete the statement. (2 points each)

_____ **26.** Drugs may lead to _____ , which is a state in which the user experiences physical dependence on drugs.

_____ **27.** A person suffering from post-traumatic stress disorder experiences again a catastrophe in the form of dreams or _____ .

_____ **28.** Psychogenic _____ involves a failure to remember past experiences.

_____ **29.** A transformation of emotional difficulties into the loss of a specific physiological function is called a(n) _____ .

_____ **30.** Amnesia coupled with active flight is called _____ .

_____ **31.** A(n) _____ involves a person thinking the same thoughts over and over again.

_____ **32.** False beliefs maintained in the face of contrary evidence are called _____ .

_____ **33.** There are data that suggest that people may inherit a(n) _____ , or tendency, to develop schizophrenia.

_____ **34.** The sociopath is an example of a(n) _____ personality.

_____ **35.** DSM-IV uses five major dimensions, or _____ , to evaluate individuals.

Directions: Match each person or term in the left column with the best association. Write the letter of the association in the space provided. (2 points each)

_____ **36.** delusion

_____ **37.** hallucination

_____ **38.** conversion disorder

_____ **39.** major depressive disorder

_____ **40.** dissociative disorder

_____ **41.** psychogenic fugue

_____ **42.** antisocial personality

_____ **43.** psychological dependence

_____ **44.** somatoform disorder

_____ **45.** post-traumatic stress disorder

a. form of hysteria in which an individual exhibits a loss of memory of identity

b. use of a drug to such an extent that an individual feels anxious without it

c. condition in which an individual sometimes assumes a new identity

d. false belief maintained in face of contrary evidence

e. phenomenon in which victim of catastrophe experiences again the original event in flashbacks

f. form of hysteria characterized by changing emotional difficulties into a loss of specific body function

g. perceptions that have no direct external cause

h. mental disturbance marked by physical symptoms for which no apparent cause exists

i. severe form of depression that interferes with functioning and well-being

j. personality disorder characterized by irresponsibility, shallow emotions and lack of conscience

Directions: Answer the following questions on a separate sheet of paper. (5 points each)

46. Explain what a psychoactive substance use disorder is.

47. Discuss the difference between a panic disorder and a phobic disorder.

Test

CHAPTER
16

Form A

THERAPY AND CHANGE

Directions: In the space at the left, write the letter of the choice that best completes the statement or answers the question. (2 points each)

_____ 1. According to Freudian analysis, a patient who impedes the course of therapy by refusing to reveal the details of a family battle that occurred during his childhood is displaying
  a. suppression
  b. resistance
  c. transference
  d. reaction formation

_____ 2. In which of the following is the goal to help clients become more flexible by developing more effective adult ego-state responses?
  a. psychoanalysis
  b. behavior therapy
  c. transactional analysis
  d. client-centered therapy

_____ 3. A client goes to a therapist because he is terrified of all social situations and stays in his room most of the time. The therapist teaches the client to relax and then has him make a list of all the frightening aspects of social situations. They then work through the list from the least frightening to the most frightening situation. This is an example of
  a. stimulus generalization
  b. aversive conditioning
  c. systematic desensitization
  d. extinction management

_____ 4. Which of the following is not true of encounter groups?
  a. they are primarily for "normal" people who want to enrich their lives
  b. they employ a number of techniques, including role playing
  c. they are, at worst, harmless
  d. they attempt to help people live more intense lives

_____ 5. For a long time the only kind of psychotherapy practiced in Western society was
  a. psychoanalysis
  b. behaviorism
  c. client-centered therapy
  d. existential therapy

_____ 6. Which of the following is not necessarily a characteristic of a good therapist?
  a. reasonably psychologically healthy individual
  b. capacity for warmth and understanding
  c. interested in conducting research
  d. experienced in dealing with people

7. A patient finds that the feelings of hatred he had for his father he now feels toward his therapist. According to psychoanalytic theory, this phenomenon is an example of
   a. displacement
   b. conversion
   c. regression
   d. transference

8. Which of the following theorists stresses the need to help people overcome their fear of freedom?
   a. Albert Ellis
   b. Sigmund Freud
   c. Fritz Perls
   d. Rollo May

9. An elementary school teacher who allows those students who do well in their studies to play on the playground is employing the technique of
   a. stimulus generalization
   b. contingency management
   c. unconditioned reinforcement
   d. systematic desensitization

10. Which of the following is not an advantage of group therapy?
    a. it allows people to see themselves as others see them
    b. people improve their social-interaction capabilities
    c. it is more enjoyable than individual therapy
    d. it allows for better use of a therapist's time

Directions: Place a + in the space at the left of each true statement. Place a 0 at the left of each false statement. (2 points each)

11. Psychotherapy literally means "healing of the soul."

12. In order to change, it is first necessary for an individual to achieve some understanding of his or her problems.

13. Any behavior that impeded the course of therapy is called suppression.

14. Token economies are based on the principles of contingency management.

15. Amphetamines have been proven to be remarkably effective in alleviating anxiety.

16. One of the major functions of psychotherapy is to help people realize that they can always rely on someone else to help with their problems.

17. A patient's view as to whether he or she can be helped may have an impact on the success of his or her psychotherapy.

18. People who have a great deal in common with their therapists are more likely than those who don't to have successful experiences in therapy.

_____ **19.** The three most influential approaches to psychotherapy are psychoanalysis, the human potential movement, and EST.

_____ **20.** The technique in which patients talk about everything that comes to mind is called free association.

_____ **21.** Gestalt therapy was developed by Viktor Frankl.

_____ **22.** Transactional analysis begins with a contract between therapist and client.

_____ **23.** A therapist who uses the technique of systematic desensitization is probably a person-centered therapist.

_____ **24.** The first step for a client involved in rational-emotive therapy is to realize that some of his or her assumptions are false.

_____ **25.** Ellis theorizes that emotion problems arise when assumptions are unrealistic.

Directions: In the space at the left, write the term or terms that best complete the statement. (2 points each)

_____ **26.** In some medical and psychological quarters, psychological disturbance is seen as the _____ of a disease.

_____ **27.** _____ are usually medical doctors who take special training in Freudian theory and techniques.

_____ **28.** Therapy is most effective with an introspective person who can tolerate _____ .

_____ **29.** In psychoanalysis, an understanding of unconscious motives is called _____ .

_____ **30.** Anything that impedes the course of treatment is _____ .

_____ **31.** Person-centered therapy is based on _____ theory.

_____ **32.** _____ therapy emphasizes the here-and-now.

_____ **33.** In _____ therapy the emphasis is on action, not insight.

_____ **34.** The process of placing an individual in a mental hospital is called _____ .

_____ **35.** The method of behavior therapy used to overcome irrational fears and anxieties is _____ .

Directions: Match each term in the right column with the best association. Write the letter of the association in the space provided. (2 points each)

_____ **36.** psychiatrist

_____ **37.** free association

_____ **38.** person-centered therapy

_____ **39.** existential therapy

_____ **40.** Gestalt therapy

_____ **41.** rational-emotive therapy

_____ **42.** transactional analysis

_____ **43.** behavior therapy

_____ **44.** group therapy

_____ **45.** eclectic

a. AA

b. multifaceted approach

c. Berne

d. Ellis

e. Frankl

f. medical doctor

g. Perls

h. psychoanalysis

i. Rogers

j. systematic desensitization

Directions: Answer the following questions on a separate sheet of paper. (5 points each)

46. Discuss the characteristics of psychotherapy in general.

47. How do behavior therapists and psychoanalysts differ in their therapeutic approaches?

Test

CHAPTER 16

Form B

THERAPY AND CHANGE

Directions: In the space at the left, write the letter of the choice that best completes the statement or answers the question. (2 points each)

_____ 1. Which psychotherapist believes that feelings of emptiness and boredom are the primary source of emotional problems?
a. Freud
b. Frankl
c. Rogers
d. Laing

_____ 2. A therapist who follows the theories of Sigmund Freud is likely to encourage his or her patients to talk about everything that comes to mind. This method is called
a. free association
b. insight
c. transference
d. displacement

_____ 3. Which therapist emphasized the relationship between the patient and the therapist in the here-and-now?
a. Fritz Perls
b. Sigmund Freud
c. B. F. Skinner
d. Viktor Frankl

_____ 4. Which type of psychotherapy is based on the belief that emotional problems arise when an individual's assumptions are unrealistic?
a. person-centered
b. psychoanalysis
c. contingency management
d. rational-emotive

_____ 5. Which of the following statements is not true concerning psychotherapy?
a. the primary goal is to strengthen the patient's control over his or her life
b. a major task of therapy is to help the patient find alternatives to his or her present unsatisfactory ways of behaving
c. the success of therapy is dependent on the skill of the therapist and not on the patient's attitude
d. in order to change, a patient must develop an understanding of his or her troubles

_____ 6. Which of the following types of therapy is a part of the human potential movement?
a. psychoanalysis
b. behavior therapy
c. existential therapy
d. all of the above

_____ 7. Suppose, by some strange set of circumstances, you are able to overhear a therapy session between a patient and a therapist. You notice that a great deal of time is spent discussing the patient's dreams and experiences she had as a child. This information would lead you to believe that the therapist most likely believes in
a. psychoanalysis
b. behavior therapy
c. person-centered therapy
d. existential therapy

_____ 8. Which of the following statements is not true of person-centered therapy?
   a. person-centered therapists assume that people are basically good
   b. person-centered therapists believe people to be capable of handling their own lives
   c. person-centered therapists offer their own opinions to people who come to them for therapy
   d. person-centered therapy is conducted in an atmosphere of emotional support

_____ 9. The theorist who originated rational-emotive therapy is
   a. Fritz Perls   c. Albert Ellis
   b. Rollo May   d. B. F. Skinner

_____ 10. Which of the following statements is not true of Alcoholics Anonymous?
   a. AA believes that drinkers must learn to solve their own problems
   b. every member must be willing to come to the aid of another member who is tempted to take a drink
   c. in order to change, an alcoholic must admit that he or she is powerless over alcohol
   d. all of the above

Directions: Place a + in the space at the left of each true statement. Place a 0 at the left of each false statement. (2 points each)

_____ 11. People who think of themselves as mentally ill often see themselves in a passive helpless position.

_____ 12. Statistics prove, without a doubt, that just as many people improve without psychotherapy as with it.

_____ 13. According to the existentialists, freedom and autonomy are nonthreatening for most, if not all, of us.

_____ 14. Rational-emotive therapy aims to correct false and self-defeating beliefs.

_____ 15. It is possible for a patient's condition to worsen or remain unchanged in a mental hospital.

_____ 16. The process of therapy is usually relaxing and enjoyable.

_____ 17. Psychotherapy is the best form of therapy for everyone.

_____ 18. The people who benefitted most from psychotherapy are those who have relatively mild problems.

_____ 19. Psychoanalysis has evolved to the point that it allows most patients to make fundamental life changes within six months.

_____ 20. Person-centered therapy is based on the theories of Erich Fromm.

_____ 21. Transactional analysis was introduced by Eric Berne.

_____ **22.** Behavior therapists spend a good deal of time exploring a client's past history.

_____ **23.** As in psychoanalysis, a Gestalt therapist would look for incidents in the past that are making the present unbearable for a client.

_____ **24.** Psychoanalysis is a relatively new form of psychotherapy.

_____ **25.** Most patients in mental hospitals have committed themselves voluntarily.

Directions: In the space at the left, write the term or terms that best complete the statement. (2 points each)

_____ **26.** The influence of a patient's hopes and expectations on therapeutic progress is called the _____ effect.

_____ **27.** _____ are medical doctors who specialize in the treatment of mental illness.

_____ **28.** Psychoanalysis is based on the theories of _____ .

_____ **29.** The talking method used in psychoanalysis is called _____ .

_____ **30.** The human potential movement has its roots in _____ psychology.

_____ **31.** According to _____ , feelings of emptiness and boredom are the source of emotional problems.

_____ **32.** Assumptions about life are the core of _____ therapy.

_____ **33.** _____ are individuals who provide psychological aid although they have had little or no formal training in counseling.

_____ **34.** _____ programs help people deal with emergencies and stressful situations.

_____ **35.** The process, experienced by the patient, of feeling toward an analyst the way he or she feels toward an important figure in his or her life is called _____ .

Directions: Match each person or term in the left column with the best association. Write the letter of the association in the space provided. (2 points each)

_____ **36.** empathy

a. form of behavior therapy in which desired behavior is reinforced

_____ **37.** insight

b. method used to examine the unconscious

_____ **38.** resistance

c. general term for any treatment undertaken by professionals to help troubled individuals overcome their problems

_____ **39.** ego states

d. method that combines many different kinds of therapy

_____ **40.** psychotherapy

e. reluctance of a patient to examine long-standing behavior patterns

_____ **41.** neuroleptic

f. atmosphere of emotional support

_____ **42.** free association

g. sudden realization of a solution

_____ **43.** eclectic approach

h. capacity for warmth and understanding

_____ **44.** contingency management

i. drugs used in treatment of schizophrenia

_____ **45.** unconditional positive regard

j. phrase used in TA theory to describe way people organize their thoughts, feelings, and actions

Directions: Answer the following questions on a separate sheet of paper. (5 points each)

46. Discuss the research on the effectiveness of psychotherapy.

47. Compare and contrast behavior therapy, rational-emotive therapy, and transactional analysis.

CHAPTER 17 Test
HUMAN INTERACTION

Form A

Directions: In the space at the left, write the letter of the choice that best completes the statement or answers the question. (2 points each)

_____ 1. A friend knows as much about music and dance as you do. In terms of reward values for friendship, she has
  a. stimulation value
  b. utility value
  c. proximity value
  d. ego-support value

_____ 2. Important factors in choosing friends include
  a. physical proximity
  b. reward value
  c. similarity
  d. all of the above

_____ 3. You have just met someone who seems highly intelligent. You also assume that she is ambitious, highly motivated, and active. This is an example of
  a. character traits
  b. norms
  c. implicit personality theory
  d. social place

_____ 4. In the Leavitt experiment on communication patterns, the slowest at solving the problem but the happiest group was the
  a. wheel
  b. circle
  c. chain
  d. Y

_____ 5. In the Robber's Cave experiment
  a. competitive athletic events led to cooperation
  b. differences between the groups were settled by fun activities
  c. the two groups did not come together
  d. emergencies requiring cooperation led to the groups coming together

_____ 6. Laura is in a state of high anxiety. She is given the chance of waiting alone or with others. According to research, she most likely will prefer to wait
  a. alone
  b. with others who are not anxious
  c. with others who are experiencing a similar type of anxiety
  d. with others who are experiencing a different type of anxiety

_____ 7. The best single predictor of whether or not people will become friends is their
  a. liking each other's looks
  b. living close to each other
  c. having similar interests
  d. being of the same religion

_____ 8. Which of the following would not be considered a psychological group?
  a. a basketball team
  b. the citizens of the U.S.A.
  c. passengers in an elevator
  d. members of a family

_____ 9. Which of the following is not an ideological group?
  a. the Communist party
  b. the National Organization for Women
  c. the New York Yankees
  d. the NAACP

_____ 10. Nonverbal communication could involve
  a. smiling
  b. body language
  c. eye contact
  d. all of the above

Directions: Place a + in the space at the left of each true statement. Place a 0 at the left of each false statement. (2 points each)

_____ 11. Clinical psychologists study the circumstances that intensify our desire for human contact.

_____ 12. The bubble of privacy is larger for Germans than for Arabs.

_____ 13. The most important variable in establishing friendship is reward value.

_____ 14. People are keenly aware of the nonverbal messages they are sending.

_____ 15. Physical appearance is a factor in both same and opposite sex relationships.

_____ 16. The task leader usually commands the group's loyalty.

_____ 17. The use of body language is a conscious process.

_____ 18. In the Schachter study, the women in the high anxiety group preferred to wait with others.

_____ 19. Husbands and wives tend to have similar educational backgrounds.

_____ 20. Americans carry a bubble of privacy around themselves much smaller than that of Arab people.

_____ 21. Common goals are prerequisites for group independence.

_____ **22.** People who work together usually maintain a public distance.

_____ **23.** The smaller the group, the less individual responsibility each member feels.

_____ **24.** The socioeconomic status of an adolescent's peer group affects his or her vocational plans.

_____ **25.** Proximity does not ensure lasting friendships.

Directions: In the space at the left, write the term or terms that best complete the statement. (2 points each)

_____ **26.** _____ psychologists study the situations that intensify our need for human contact.

_____ **27.** Psychologists have demonstrated that people get together to reduce their _____ about themselves.

_____ **28.** Sympathy and approval are elements of a(n) _____ value friendship.

_____ **29.** An imaginative friend provides _____ value.

_____ **30.** Because we belong to different groups, each of us has multiple _____ that change.

_____ **31.** Hall found that Americans let only intimates closer than _____ inches.

_____ **32.** _____ is an attempt to understand how we interpret people's behavior.

_____ **33.** Exaggerated assumptions about people in an identifiable category are called _____ .

_____ **34.** A team of construction workers is a(n) _____ oriented group.

_____ **35.** Assuming that someone else will take action in an emergency is called _____ .

Directions: Match each person or term in the left column with the best association. Write the letter of the association in the space provided. (2 points each)

_____ 36. interesting or imaginative friend   **a.** assumptions about others

_____ 37. cooperative and helpful friend   **b.** emotional appeal

_____ 38. Hall   **c.** group conflict

_____ 39. attribution theory   **d.** group formation

_____ 40. interdependence   **e.** group structure

_____ 41. sociogram   **f.** interpreting people's actions

_____ 42. charisma   **g.** like and love

_____ 43. Rubin   **h.** social space

_____ 44. Robber's Cave experiment   **i.** stimulation value

_____ 45. implicit personality theory   **j.** utility value

Directions: Answer the following questions on a separate sheet of paper. (5 points each)

46. Frequently, an individual is attacked in public while witnesses stand by and do nothing. Describe some of the psychological phenomena that might be responsible for a witness's failure to come to the aid of someone in distress.

47. Discuss the variables that enter into perceiving other people.

Test

HUMAN INTERACTION

Form B

Directions: In the space at the left, write the letter of the choice that best completes the statement or answers the question. (2 points each)

_____ 1. Schachter's experiment showed that high anxiety produced a need for
    a. isolation
    b. human contact
    c. shock therapy
    d. increased stimulation

_____ 2. Hall's studies on the "bubble of privacy" indicate that
    a. people in all cultures give each other the same amount of social space
    b. Americans are more likely to stand close to each other than are Arabs
    c. Germans require more social space than Americans
    d. Americans require more social space than Germans

_____ 3. Public distance is
    a. 3-10 feet
    b. more than 10 feet
    c. 9-36 inches
    d. less than 9 inches

_____ 4. Which of the following is not generally a true description of leaders?
    a. they are better adjusted than the rest of the group
    b. they are more self-confident than the rest of the group
    c. they are more intelligent than the rest of the group
    d. they are more outgoing than the rest of the group

_____ 5. The tendency to assume that someone else will handle emergencies when more than one person is present is called
    a. group cooperation
    b. group dynamics
    c. confusion of roles
    d. diffusion of responsibility

_____ 6. In the Gerard and Rabbie experiment, which group preferred to wait alone?
    a. those who knew their scores but not those of others
    b. those who knew both their own scores and those of others
    c. those who received no information about their scores
    d. those who knew the scores of others but not their own

_____ 7. A friend spends long hours helping you master French. She has _____ value.
    a. proximity
    b. utility
    c. stimulation
    d. ego-support

_____ 8. The study of our need for contact and interaction with other human beings is the domain of
    a. clinical psychology
    b. social psychology
    c. developmental psychology
    d. personal psychology

_____ **9.** When a person claims personal responsibility for an achievement, it may be a case of
    a. stereotyping
    b. implicit personality theory
    c. actor-observer bias
    d. self-serving bias

_____ **10.** Several passengers in an elevator may become a group if
    a. the elevator suddenly becomes stuck between floors
    b. they are of the same sex
    c. they are all close in age
    d. each has the same floor as a destination

Directions: Place a + in the space at the left of each true statement. Place a 0 at the left of each false statement. (2 points each)

_____ **11.** The most important variable in establishing friendship is reward value.

_____ **12.** Most people play a single role throughout their lives.

_____ **13.** Clinical psychologists study the circumstances that intensify our desire for human contact.

_____ **14.** Appreciation and support in friendships are examples of utility value.

_____ **15.** The use of body language is a conscious process.

_____ **16.** Common goals are prerequisites for group interdependence.

_____ **17.** Forming an impression of a person is an active process.

_____ **18.** Men and women seek out the most attractive members of their social worlds.

_____ **19.** In the Schachter study, the women in the high anxiety group preferred to wait with others.

_____ **20.** People at a party usually maintain a social distance.

_____ **21.** The size of a bubble of privacy is the same for all cultures.

_____ **22.** In most groups, task and social functions are easily separated.

_____ **23.** Leavitt's "circle" group was the slowest at problem solving.

_____ **24.** The smaller the group, the less individual responsibility each member feels.

_____ **25.** Personal sacrifice decreases commitment to a group.

Directions: In the space at the left, write the term or terms that best complete the statement.
(2 points each)

_____ **26.** Schachter demonstrated that high anxiety produced a need for _____ .

_____ **27.** A friend who aids you in reaching a goal provides _____ value.

_____ **28.** We each have our own implicit personality theory— a set of _____ about how people behave.

_____ **29.** Some married couples seem to have _____ needs rather than similar ones.

_____ **30.** Hall found that a distance of more than _____ feet does not invite personal communication.

_____ **31.** The psychologist _____ studied the idea of personal space in various cultures.

_____ **32.** A _____ is a diagram representing relationships within a group.

_____ **33.** A leader is concerned with both _____ and the welfare of the workers.

_____ **34.** A(n) _____ is characterized by interdependence, shared goals and communication.

_____ **35.** People usually choose friends whose backgrounds are _____ to their own.

Directions: Match each person or term in the left column with the best association. Write the letter of the association in the space provided. (2 points each)

_____ **36.** norms

_____ **37.** stereotype

_____ **38.** task function

_____ **39.** social functions

_____ **40.** ideology

_____ **41.** nonverbal communication

_____ **42.** physical proximity

_____ **43.** self-serving bias

_____ **44.** actor-observer bias

_____ **45.** fundamental attribution error

a. inclination to attribute others' behavior to dispositional factors

b. exaggerated set of assumptions

c. tasks directed toward filling emotional needs

d. tendency to claim success is based on own efforts

e. common ideas, attitudes, and goals

f. distance from one another people live and work

g. process of communicating through use of space, body language, and facial expression

h. tendency to attribute one's own behavior to outside causes rather than to a personality trait

i. group functions directed toward getting a job done

j. rules for behavior

Directions: Answer the following questions on a separate sheet of paper. (5 points each)

46. Discuss and give examples of the concept of personal space.

47. Frequently, an individual is attacked in public while witnesses stand by and do nothing. Describe some of the psychological phenomena that might be responsible for a witness's failure to come to the aid of someone in distress.

CHAPTER 18 Test

Form A

ATTITUDES AND SOCIAL INFLUENCE

Directions: In the space at the left, write the letter of the choice that best completes the statement or answers the question. (2 points each)

_____ 1. Which of the following is not true in regard to attitudes?
   a. they are based on personal knowledge of the issue, person, or thing
   b. they are determined by our culture
   c. our parents generally have a large impact on our attitudes
   d. they are in line with the attitudes of those whose approval we desire

_____ 2. The attitudes most resistant to change are those that are
   a. formed through generalization
   b. formed as a result of compliance
   c. formed through brainwashing
   d. internalized

_____ 3. A pacifist who has been drafted is against killing yet believes in obeying the law. He is probably experiencing
   a. sleeper effect
   b. boomerang effect
   c. inoculation effect
   d. cognitive dissonance

_____ 4. Another word for prejudice is
   a. discrimination
   b. negativism
   c. prejudgment
   d. stereotyping

_____ 5. The fact that some people are persuaded by a message only after some time is called the
   a. inoculation effect
   b. sleeper effect
   c. boomerang effect
   d. brainwashing

_____ 6. The Asch study showed that
   a. people will conform to a group even if it goes against their better judgment
   b. people will obey authority
   c. very few people conform to group decisions if they know them to be wrong
   d. only weak people conform to group decisions

_____ 7. Acting on a prejudice is called
   a. stereotyping
   b. discrimination
   c. compliance
   d. generalization

_____ 8. Which of the following is not a main element of attitudes?
   a. beliefs
   b. feelings
   c. inflexibility
   d. tendencies

_____ 9. A man who hires women for high-level positions even though he firmly believes that they belong in the home is exhibiting
   a. internalization
   b. identification
   c. compliance
   d. rationalization

_____ 10. The subjects in the Milgram experiment were
   a. not representative of the average American
   b. sadistic
   c. ordinary working people
   d. not uncomfortable with administering the shock

Directions: Place a + in the space at the left of each true statement. Place a 0 at the left of each false statement. (2 points each)

_____ 11. One of the basic components of an attitude is a tendency to act toward something in a certain way.

_____ 12. Attitudes adopted because of identification with a group are likely to last even after the individual leaves the group.

_____ 13. Internalization is most likely to occur when an attitude is consistent with a person's basic beliefs and values and supports his or her self-image.

_____ 14. The source of the message is one part of the communication puzzle.

_____ 15. One way to avoid dissonance is to avoid situations or exposure to information that would create conflict.

_____ 16. The sleeper effect is the delayed impact or attitude change of a persuasive communication.

_____ 17. Attitudes are not normally culturally derived.

_____ 18. Compliance will never lead to internalization of an attitude.

_____ 19. Identification occurs when a person wants to define himself or herself in terms of a person or group.

_____ 20. Prejudice is not always negative.

_____ 21. People are usually prejudiced against those less well-off than themselves.

_____ 22. The study concerning cognitive dissonance actually resulted in some subjects changing their attitudes toward civil rights.

_____ 23. When presenting an argument it is usually more effective to present both sides of the issue.

_____ 24. Efforts at persuasion usually have their greatest impact after a few days have elapsed rather than immediately.

_____ 25. Effects from brainwashing persist after a prisoner is released.

Directions: In the space at the left, write the term or terms that best complete the statement. (2 points each)

_____ 26. When we give in to the wishes of others to avoid discomfort, it is called _____ .

_____ 27. Wholehearted acceptance of an attitude is called _____ .

_____ 28. Beliefs, feelings, and tendencies to act are the components of _____ .

_____ 29. A belief that operates to bring about its own fulfillment is a(n) _____ .

_____ 30. The unequal treatment of members of certain groups is called _____ .

_____ 31. Cognitive _____ is an uncomfortable feeling that arises when conflicting thoughts, attitudes, or feelings exist within a person.

_____ 32. The _____ effect is the time lag between message and impact.

_____ 33. The most famous study on obedience was done by _____ .

_____ 34. When people dislike the source of a message the _____ effect may occur.

_____ 35. The need to _____ forces people to abandon stereotyped ideas.

Directions: Match each person or term in the left column with the best association. Write the letter of the association in the space provided. (2 points each)

_____ **36.** attitude

_____ **37.** internalization

_____ **38.** Devine

_____ **39.** discrimination

_____ **40.** Festinger

_____ **41.** Lifton

_____ **42.** sleeper effect

_____ **43.** inoculation effect

_____ **44.** Asch

_____ **45.** Milgram

a. study on brainwashing

b. studies on relationships between stereotypes and prejudice

c. cognitive dissonance

d. conformity

e. delayed attitude change

f. obedience to authority

g. predisposition to respond

h. unequal treatment

i. wholehearted acceptance of attitude

j. method of developing resistance to persuasion

Directions: Answer the following questions on a separate sheet of paper. (5 points each)

46. From your reading on persuasion, discuss the best way to get an idea across.

47. Explain what attitudes are and describe how they are formed and how they are changed.

CHAPTER 18 Test

Form B

ATTITUDES AND SOCIAL INFLUENCE

Directions: In the space at the left, write the letter of the choice that best completes the statement or answers the question. (2 points each)

_____ 1. A young boy idolizes an uncle who is a strong believer in socialism. The boy then begins to express socialist ideas that resemble those of his uncle. This is an example of
    a. brainwashing   **c.** internalization
    b. identification   **d.** compliance

_____ 2. The target of misplaced aggression is
    a. discrimination   **c.** the scapegoat
    b. negativism   **d.** stereotyping

_____ 3. According to the text, the communication process consists of _____ parts.
    a. 3   **c.** 7
    b. 4   **d.** 8

_____ 4. Our expectations affecting other people's actions is called
    a. the sleeper effect   **c.** the inoculation effect
    b. the boomerang effect   **d.** behavioral confirmation

_____ 5. The result of the Milgram study showed that
    a. people are basically sadistic
    b. people obey authority figures beyond reasonable limits
    c. the majority of people will not perform acts against their will
    d. most people will conform to group pressure

_____ 6. Strategies such as the "foot-in-the-door" technique are aimed at influencing the
    a. source   **c.** message
    b. channel   **d.** audience

_____ 7. Incorporating attitudes into a person's belief system is called
    a. stereotyping   **c.** internalization
    b. brainwashing   d. prejudice

_____ 8. Asch's experiment showed that
    a. the communication process is made up of four parts
    b. conformity to pressure by peers has strong effect
    c. the effects of persuasion are usually short-lived
    d. none of the above

_____ 9. _____ influence attitudes.
    a. Culture   **c.** Parents
    b. Peers   **d.** All of the above

_____ **10.** You believe all conservative people to be cold and aloof. When you meet a conservative you keep your distance, then the person seems to act cold toward you. This is an example of
   a. self-justification
   b. self-fulfilling prophecy
   c. boomerang effect
   d. inoculation effect

Directions: Place a + in the space at the left of each true statement. Place a 0 at the left of each false statement. (2 points each)

_____ **11.** Stereotyping and discrimination mean the same thing.

_____ **12.** Internalization is incorporating new beliefs into one's own belief system.

_____ **13.** Prejudice is judging people on the basis of stereotypes.

_____ **14.** Prejudice and discrimination are synonymous.

_____ **15.** Milgram's experiment showed that obedience to authority is a weakly held belief.

_____ **16.** According to one view, discrimination is a result of displaced aggression.

_____ **17.** Parental influence on children's attitudes wanes as the children get older.

_____ **18.** Attitudes based upon identification are fragile.

_____ **19.** In both identification and compliance, the individual doesn't really believe the attitude he or she expresses.

_____ **20.** The most extreme form of attitude change is compliance.

_____ **21.** Dissonance reduction is always a conscious process.

_____ **22.** A candidate for public office is advised by her campaign organization to project a youthful, energetic image. As it turns out, the voters are more likely to vote for a person who conveys an image of wisdom and the stability of age and experience. The candidate thus loses the election. This is an example of the boomerang effect.

_____ **23.** According to the study conducted in Ann Arbor, Michigan, advertisements in the media were more effective than personal contacts.

_____ **24.** Zimbardo's findings confirmed the false-consensus effect.

_____ **25.** People will not obey an authority figure whose instructions go against their own standards of moral behavior.

Directions: In the space at the left, write the term or terms that best complete the statement. (2 points each)

_____ 26. The _____ is the person or group from which a message originates.

_____ 27. A group that has become the target of another is called a(n) _____ .

_____ 28. _____ is the need to rationalize one's attitudes and behavior.

_____ 29. The person or persons receiving a message are the _____ .

_____ 30. The means by which a message is transmitted is the _____ .

_____ 31. The actual content transmitted to an audience is the _____ .

_____ 32. The most extreme method of attitude change is _____ .

_____ 33. _____ route processing occurs when the recipient of a message thoughtfully considers the arguments.

_____ 34. _____ route processing occurs when the recipient of a message considers cues other than the message itself.

_____ 35. _____ means prejudgment.

Directions: Match each person or term in the left column with the best association. Write the letter of the association in the space provided. (2 points each)

_____ **36.** source

_____ **37.** message

_____ **38.** channel

_____ **39.** audience

_____ **40.** compliance

_____ **41.** brainwashing

_____ **42.** prejudice

_____ **43.** boomerang effect

_____ **44.** identification

_____ **45.** persuasion

a. the person or group from which a message originates

b. the process of seeing oneself as similar to another person or group

c. change in attitude or behavior opposite to one desired by persuader

d. the means by which a message is transmitted

e. the direct attempt to influence attitudes

f. actual content transmitted to audience

g. the most extreme form of attitude change

h. preconceived attitude

i. person or persons receiving a message

j. a change of behavior in order to gain approval

Directions: Answer the following questions on a separate sheet of paper. (5 points each)

46. Describe the research on cognitive dissonance and provide examples of the phenomenon.

47. Describe how Milgram's findings on obedience to authority might be used to explain the acquiescence of the German nation to Hitlerism.

CHAPTER 19 Test

Form A

PSYCHOLOGY: PRESENT AND FUTURE

Directions: In the space at the left, write the letter of the choice that best completes the statement or answers the question. (2 points each)

_____ 1. When injected in elderly adults, human growth hormone
a. seems to stop the aging process
b. increases the rate of aging
c. has well-determined, long-term effects
d. does not impact body fat or muscle mass

_____ 2. While the Ph.D. is traditionally a research-based degree, clinical psychologists have developed another form of doctorate called a _____ that concentrates primarily on mastering skills in testing, interviewing, and therapy.
a. J.D.
b. Ther.D.
c. Psy.D.
d. Pt.D.

_____ 3. One of the age groups that is expected to show significant increases in size during the first half of the 21st century is those _____ years old.
a. 10-20
b. 25-45
c. 45-65
d. more than 60

_____ 4. Applying the principles of psychology may require not even a high school degree in jobs such as a _____ or may require a Ph.D. such as a _____ must have.
a. mental health assistant; personnel director
b. ward attendant; psychotherapist
c. high school psychology teacher; salesperson
d. crisis hotline adviser; school psychologist

_____ 5. B. F. Skinner's controversial best-seller *Beyond Freedom and Dignity* posed the idea of substituting _____ for punishment as the primary means to keep people obeying the laws of society.
a. psychology
b. a service-based economy
c. operant principles
d. reinforcement

_____ 6. In designing the dashboard of lunar landing modules to assure efficient communication of information, NASA would most likely call on a(n) _____ psychologist.
a. consulting
b. psychoanalytic
c. engineering
d. forensic

_____ 7. The largest proportion of psychologists are involved in
  a. teaching psychology
  b. mental health services
  c. counseling
  d. developmental psychology

_____ 8. Perhaps more than another other, Clifford Beers's book _____ , contributed to the establishment of our modern concerns for the mentally ill.
  a. *A Mind That Found Itself*
  b. *Beyond Freedom and Dignity*
  c. *Future Shock*
  d. none of the above

_____ 9. At today's mental health facilities, patients are diagnosed and stabilized, and then they are released, only to be readmitted later when they stray from their assigned treatment. This is called the _____ problem.
  a. Head Start
  b. revolving door
  c. visualization
  d. future shock

_____ 10. A psychologist studying such matters as how to select a trial jury or the impact of repeated use on an eyewitness's testimony would most likely be a(n) _____ psychologist.
  a. sports
  b. industrial-organizational
  c. human factors
  d. forensic

Directions: Place a + in the space at the left of each true statement. Place a 0 at the left of each false statement. (2 points each)

_____ 11. Money invested in the Head Start program to educate disadvantaged children is more than offset by savings in social services not required by Head Start graduates.

_____ 12. Psychology is a good college major for someone planning graduate work in law or medicine.

_____ 13. Engineering psychologists work to improve methods of worker selection and training.

_____ 14. Daniel Levinson's *The Seasons of a Man's Life* details the stages and crises of a typical man's life.

_____ 15. Alvin Toffler argues for the importance of shifting the world's economy toward consumption of raw materials rather than service.

_____ 16. Physiological psychologists apply psychological principles to human-machine interactions.

_____ 17. Forensic psychologists deal with efficient operation in business and industry.

_____ 18. Many athletes use a process called visualization to help them improve their performance.

_____ 19. The top three killers of children through the period of adolescence are medical problems.

_____ 20. Dedication and personal responsibility are more important than educational level achieved by the best crisis hotline advisers.

_____ 21. Psychologists have played a major role in improving the value and accuracy of intellectual test results.

_____ 22. Psychology will be among the slowest-growing fields in the early 21st century.

_____ 23. Day care appears to have many negative effects on children.

_____ 24. French physician Philippe Pinel was among the first to view the mentally deranged as ill rather than possessed.

_____ 25. Psychologists study and emphasize human growth, development, personality, performance, and performance limits.

Directions: In the space at the left, write the term or terms that best complete the statement. (2 points each)

_____ 26. _____ was among the earliest television programs in which psychologists had a major impact on program content.

_____ 27. More than half of all _____ and _____ work outside the home.

_____ 28. Three major professional and scientific associations of psychologists and educations include _____ , _____ , and _____ .

_____ 29. Properly designed controls for equipment are positioned first based on their _____ and then on the frequency with which they are used.

_____ 30. Athletic performance can be enhanced through _____ .

_____ 31. The Scholastic Assessment Test (SAT) was redesigned in 1994 to give more weight to _____ .

_____ 32. A person with a Psy.D. would most likely be a _____ psychologist.

_____ 33. The National Committee for Mental Hygiene eventually organized the _____ .

_____ **34.** Reducing AIDS, violence, and drug use requires changes in our _____ .

_____ **35.** Three names often associated with improving treatment for the mentally ill are Philippe Pinel, Clifford Beers, and _____ .

Directions: Match each person or term in the left column with the best association. Write the letter of the association in the space provided. (2 points each)

_____ **36.** Connecticut Society for Mental Hygiene

_____ **37.** gerontology

_____ **38.** forensic psychologist

_____ **39.** personnel director

_____ **40.** Dorothea Dix

_____ **41.** American Psychological Association

_____ **42.** engineering psychologist

_____ **43.** Alvin Toffler

_____ **44.** applied psychologists

_____ **45.** day care children

a. machines

b. swap consumption for service

c. assertive, aggressive

d. study of medicine, law, social work, education, or psychology

e. Clifford Beers

f. campaigned for improved treatment for mentally ill

g. organizational and quantitative skills

h. solving human problems

i. criminal behavior

j. study of aging

Directions: Answer the following questions on a separate sheet of paper. (5 points each)

46. Summarize Alvin Toffler's arguments that he advanced in his book *Future Shock.* Do you agree with his concerns? Why or why not?

47. Describe a variety of jobs that could be held by someone with an education in psychology, and identify the level of education needed to hold each of the jobs you describe.

Test

Form B

PSYCHOLOGY: PRESENT AND FUTURE

Directions: In the space at the left, write the letter of the choice that best completes the statement or answers the question. (2 points each)

_____ 1. Philippe Pinel's efforts led to more humane treatment of the mentally ill in
    a. Canada   **c.** Germany
    b. France   **d.** the United States

_____ 2. Applying psychological principles to human-machine interaction is the domain of
    a. educational psychologists
    b. ward attendants
    c. engineering psychologists
    d. all of the above

_____ 3. Research on the effects of day care supports the idea that
    a. children who do not attend day care tend to be more assertive and aggressive
    b. day care appears to have many negative effects on children
    c. day care promotes development of social skills
    d. none of the above

_____ 4. Harry Harlow's studies led to the theory that
    a. day-care children think at a more advanced level
    b. the elderly population will continue to grow
    c. the SAT needed to be revised
    d. the attachment of children to their caregivers is made stronger by physical contact

_____ 5. Current projections indicate that the population of men and women more than 60 years of age will
    a. begin decreasing
    b. show minimal growth
    c. continue to grow
    d. level off after the first decade of the 21st century

_____ 6. All of contemporary psychology can be grouped into
    a. experimental and applied fields
    b. educational and clinical psychology
    c. general and clinical psychology
    d. the divisions of psychotherapy and psychologists in private practice

_____ 7. All of the following statements about current trends in psychology are true except
    a. psychology leads all other fields in the number of minorities in the profession
    b. women hold a majority of the civilian jobs in psychology
    c. projections show that psychology should be a fast-growing field
    d. a future trend is the growth of university research jobs

8. The branch of applied psychology that studies the workings of the law is
   a. forensic psychology
   b. industrial-organizational psychology
   c. clinical psychology
   d. none of the above

9. _____ help design machines and equipment, such as computer systems, automobiles, and household appliances.
   a. Forensic psychologists
   b. Clinical psychologists
   c. Human factors engineers
   d. none of the above

10. Gerontologists are involved in the study of
    a. machines
    b. aging
    c. hormones
    d. visualization

Directions: Place a + in the space at the left of each true statement. Place a O at the left of each false statement. (2 points each)

11. Dorothea Dix was a prominent spokesperson for mental health reform in the 1800s.

12. Philippe Pinel's book *A Mind That Found Itself* was a strong force in understanding the lives of those with mental disturbances.

13. Psychologists play an important role in developing tests.

14. Clifford Beers's efforts helped pave the way for the organization of the National Association for Mental Health.

15. Projections indicate that the number of people aged 60 and older will level off after the first decade of the twenty-first century.

16. Applied psychologists put knowledge of psychology to work solving human problems.

17. The American Psychological Society is the oldest professional psychological organization in the Americas.

18. Sports psychology is a relatively new field.

19. George Miller urged psychologists to address a number of issues, including urban problems and violence.

20. All jobs in psychology or related to psychology require at least a master's degree.

21. A consulting psychologist might advise the management of a company on how to take human performance limits into account in the design of equipment.

_____ **22.** A master's degree is not required to work as a school psychologist.

_____ **23.** Projections indicate that gerontology and sports psychology will be growing fields.

_____ **24.** In *Future Shock*, Alvin Toffler argued that the operant principles of behavior could be used to better match people to their jobs.

_____ **25.** The CPA is the United States's largest professional psychological organization.

Directions: In the space at the left, write the term or terms that best complete the statement. (2 points each)

_____ **26.** A(n) _____ psychologist might help an athlete improve his or her performance through visualization.

_____ **27.** *A Mind That Found Itself*, a book by _____ , a former mental patient, was a strong force in the movement to improve mental health treatment.

_____ **28.** The 1994 version of the _____ allowed test takers the use of hand calculators for the first time.

_____ **29.** Contemporary psychology can be grouped into experimental fields and _____ fields.

_____ **30.** Elizabeth Loftus has made important contributions in the field of _____ psychology.

_____ **31.** Scientists are now able to create human growth hormone, a chemical produced by the _____ gland.

_____ **32.** In *Beyond Freedom and Dignity*, _____ argued that society should use positive reinforcers to lead people to desired behaviors.

_____ **33.** *Future Shock* described a world of depleted _____ .

_____ **34.** The American Psychological Association has a total of _____ divisions.

_____ **35.** Studies of the impact of the _____ program provides data about the effect of investment in educating economically disadvantaged children.

Directions: Match each person or term in the left column with the best association. Write the letter of the association in the space provided. (2 points each)

_____ 36. sports psychologist

    a. labor-union relations and job satisfaction

_____ 37. visualization

    b. *The Seasons of a Man's Life*

_____ 38. Philippe Pinel

    c. devises training techniques for athletes

_____ 39. Clifford Beers

    d. mentally rehearsing steps of a performance

_____ 40. CPA

    e. worked for mental health reform in France

_____ 41. B. F. Skinner

    f. *A Mind That Found Itself*

_____ 42. Daniel Levinson

    g. forerunner of the National Association for Mental Health

_____ 43. industrial-organizational psychologist

    h. professional organization founded in 1988

_____ 44. National Committee for Mental Hygiene

    i. Canadian professional organization for psychologists

_____ 45. American Psychological Society

    j. *Beyond Freedom and Dignity*

Directions: Answer the following questions on a separate sheet of paper.

46. Describe where psychologists are employed.

47. Discuss major trends that are likely to influence the future activities of psychologists.

CHAPTER 20 Test

Form A

PSYCHOLOGICAL RESEARCH AND STATISITICS

Directions: In the space at the left, write the leter of the choice that best completes the statement or answers the question. (2 points each)

_____ 1. Experiments that have been duplicated by at least one other psychologist are said to be
   a. independent
   b. intervening
   c. replicated
   d. double-blind

_____ 2. If 10 people are asked to rate a movie and the majority of them give it a very low rating, the graph of the data will
   a. show a random pattern
   b. be positively skewed
   c. be negatively skewed
   d. result in a bell-shaped curve

_____ 3. Subjects who undergo the experimental treatment are called the _____ group.
   a. control
   b. experimental
   c. do-nothing
   d. variable

_____ 4. The most commonly used measure of central tendency is the
   a. mean
   b. mode
   c. range
   d. standard deviation

_____ 5. When neither the subjects nor the experimenter knows which group of subjects is the experimental one, this is called
   a. observer effect
   b. longitudinal study
   c. single-blind procedure
   d. double-blind procedure

_____ 6. What is the mode of the following distribution: 63, 75, 75, 79, 82, 82, 84, 84, 84, 84, 91, 99?
   a. 75   c. 84
   b. 82   d. 91

_____ 7. In _____ studies, psychologists study and restudy the same group of subjects at regular intervals over a period of years.
   a. biased
   b. survey
   c. cross-cultural
   d. longitudinal

_____ **8.** A negative correlation exists if
   a. one variable causes an increase in the other variable
   b. as one variable increases, the second variable increases
   c. as one variable increases, the other variable decreases
   d. as one variable decreases, the other variable decreases

_____ **9.** The variable that experimenters manipulate is called the _____ variable.
   a. independent
   b. intervening
   c. hypothetical
   d. dependent

_____ **10.** Which of the following will always be symmetrical?
   a. histogram
   b. normal curve
   c. frequency polygon
   d. skewed distribution

Directions: Place a + in the space at the left of each true statement. Place a 0 at the left of each false statement. (2 points each)

_____ **11.** If a high rank on one measure tends to go with a low rank on another, a negative correlation exists.

_____ **12.** A normal curve is highest in the middle and tapers off toward the ends.

_____ **13.** The dependent variable is the one that experimenters manipulate so that they can observe its effect.

_____ **14.** The median score and mode score are generally the same.

_____ **15.** A sample should be representative of the population a researcher is studying.

_____ **16.** If the lowest score of a set of data is shifted lower, the mean score will not change.

_____ **17.** Naturalistic observation enables the investigator to control the situation and to eliminate the possibility that unnoticed outside factors will influence the results.

_____ **18.** A standard deviation is a more accurate measure of variability than a range.

_____ **19.** Sigmund Freud's theory of personality development was based on naturalistic observation of his patients.

_____ **20.** On a normal curve, if the distribution is very spread out, the standard deviation will tend to be large.

_____ **21.** A control group is not necessary in all experiments.

_____ **22.** Inferential statistics are useful for making generalizations about populations.

_____ **23.** No matter what the research question, an experiment is the best way to obtain an answer.

_____ **24.** In a skewed distribution, a median score more accurately reflects the average than a mean score does.

_____ **25.** A high correlation is evidence for a cause-and-effect explanation.

Directions: In the space at the left, write the term or terms that best complete the statement. (2 points each)

_____ **26.** Researchers formulate a(n) _____ , which states what they expect to find when they conduct the experiment.

_____ **27.** When the probability of a result is most unlikely to be due to chance, the result is considered to be _____ .

_____ **28.** A(n) _____ sample is one in which each individual within the scope of the research has an equal chance of being selected.

_____ **29.** Numbers that describe something about the average score are called measures of _____ .

_____ **30.** Establishing a correlation is useful because it enables scientists to make relatively accurate _____ .

_____ **31.** If you subtract the lowest score in a data set from the highest score, you are determining the _____ .

_____ **32.** An experiment enables the investigator to _____ the situation and to eliminate the possibility that unnoticed outside factors will influence the results.

_____ **33.** Sigmund Freud's theory of personality development was based on _____ studies.

_____ **34.** The subjects who are treated in the same way as the experimental group, except that the experimental treatment is not applied, are called the _____ .

_____ **35.** To determine whether the data support a hypothesis or the results are due to chance, researchers use _____ .

Directions: Match each term in the left column with the best association. Write the letter of the association in the space provided. (2 points each)

_____ **36.** population

_____ **37.** frequency distribution

_____ **38.** random sample

_____ **39.** hypothesis

_____ **40.** stratified sample

_____ **41.** mode

_____ **42.** dependent variable

_____ **43.** scatterplot

_____ **44.** cross-cultural studies

_____ **45.** skewed distribution

a. guess

b. curve whose data piles up near one end

c. changes as a result of manipulation of the independent variable

d. graph that demonstrates the direction of relationship between two variables

e. equal chance of being represented

f. investigations to determine if experiences are universal

g. most frequent score in a distribution of observations

h. representative of various subgroups of the population

i. arranging data so you know how often a score occurs

j. total group from which sample is drawn

Directions: Answer the following questions on a separate sheet of paper. (5 points each)

46. Design an experiment to test the effectiveness of a new aspirin product.

47. Explain why researchers are interested in the statistical significance of the results of their research.

CHAPTER 20 Test

Form B

PSYCHOLOGICAL RESEARCH AND STATISTICS

Directions: In the space at the left, write the letter of the choice that best completes the statement or answers the question. (2 points each)

_____ 1. A measure of the degree of relatedness between two variables is
   a. variability
   b. correlation
   c. standard deviation
   d. prediction

_____ 2. Studies in which psychologists study and restudy the same group of subjects at regular intervals over a period of years are called
   a. biased studies
   b. surveys
   c. longitudinal studies
   d. cross-cultural studies

_____ 3. The cardinal rule of naturalistic observation is to
   a. properly control the variables of the study
   b. find cooperative subjects
   c. avoid disturbing the subjects you are studying
   d. secure a stratified sample

_____ 4. The most widely used measure of variability is the
   a. standard deviation
   b. range
   c. mean
   d. Pearson correlation coefficient

_____ 5. When researchers unwittingly bring about the situation they expected to find, this is called
   a. a double-blind procedure
   b. a self-fulfilling prophecy
   c. the observer effect
   d. interpreting data

_____ 6. In the following distribution, which is the median score? 65, 78, 78, 81, 84, 92, 96
   a. 78   **c.** 82
   b. 81   **d.** 92

_____ 7. In which kind of sample does every member of the group being studied have an equal chance of being represented?
   a. stratified sample
   b. random sample
   c. biased sample
   d. all of the above

_____ **8.** A positive correlation exists if
   a. one variable causes a decrease in the other variable
   b. as one variable increases, the second variable decreases
   c. as one variable decreases, the other variable remains unchanged
   d. as one variable increases, the other variable increases

_____ **9.** Which of the following can be used to plot two sets of data at the same time?
   a. histogram
   b. normal curve
   c. frequency polygon
   d. skewed distribution

_____ **10.** In a graphed frequency distribution, the peak of the graph is the
   a. median
   b. mode
   c. range
   d. standard deviation

Directions: Place a + in the space at the left of each true statement. Place a 0 at the left of each false statement. (2 points each)

_____ **11.** If a high rank on one measure tends to go with a low rank on another, a negative correlation exists.

_____ **12.** A case study is an intensive investigation of an individual or group.

_____ **13.** The mode is the same as the median score.

_____ **14.** A median is a measure of variability.

_____ **15.** A sample should be representative of the population a researcher is studying.

_____ **16.** In a skewed distribution, the mean score will be pulled toward the most extreme scores.

_____ **17.** The first step in all psychological research is to begin gathering data about the hypothesis.

_____ **18.** A standard deviation is a more accurate measure of variability than a range.

_____ **19.** Sigmund Freud's theory of personality development was based on naturalistic observation of his patients.

_____ **20.** If you subtract the lowest score in a set of data from the highest score, you will determine the range.

_____ **21.** Case studies are an alternative to experiments in answering research questions.

_____ **22.** No matter what the research question, an experiment is the best way to obtain an answer.

_____ **23.** Inferential statistics can help researchers determine whether an outcome is due to chance.

_____ **24.** Fifty percent of scores will always fall below the mean, and 50 percent will always fall above it.

_____ **25.** A high correlation is evidence for a cause-and-effect explanation.

Directions: In the space at the left, write the term or terms that best complete the statement. (2 points each)

_____ **26.** A(n) _____ is a relatively small group out of the total population under study.

_____ **27.** The branch of mathematics that allows researchers to organize and evaluate data is called _____ .

_____ **28.** A random _____ is one in which each individual within the scope of the research has an equal chance of being selected.

_____ **29.** The mean, mode, and median are measures of _____ .

_____ **30.** The mean is what most people think of as an _____ .

_____ **31.** A coefficient with a plus sign indicates a _____ correlation.

_____ **32.** In _____ studies, the psychologist studies and restudies the same group of subjects at regular intervals over a period of years.

_____ **33.** Researchers want to know if the results of their hypotheses are statistically significant or are due to _____ .

_____ **34.** Observing how humans and animals behave without interfering is called _____ .

_____ **35.** In a negative correlation, as one variable increases, the second variable _____ .

Directions: Match each term in the left column with the best association. Write the letter of the association in the space provided.

_____ **36.** longitudinal studies

a. repeatedly gathering data on the same group of subjects over a period of time

_____ **37.** survey

b. sampling of data, obtained through inverviews and questionnaires

_____ **38.** experimental group

c. the group of subjects to which an independent variable is applied

_____ **39.** control group

d. in an experiment, the group of subjects that is treated in the same way as the experimental group, except that the experimental treatment is not applied

_____ **40.** correlation coefficient

e. a statistic that describes the direction and strength of the relationship between two sets of observations

_____ **41.** descriptive statistics

f. numerical methods used to determine whether research data support a hypothesis or whether results were due to chance

_____ **42.** inferential statistics

g. the listing and summarizing of data in a practical way

_____ **43.** median

h. the middle score

_____ **44.** normal curve

i. a measure of variability that describes an average distance of every score from the mean of the scores

_____ **45.** standard deviation

j. a symmetrical, bell-shaped curve

Directions: Answers the following questions on a separate sheet of paper. (5 points each)

46. An almost random sampling of a city may be obtained by taking every twentieth name in the phone book. In what ways is the method described not purely random?

47. Design an experiment to test the effectiveness of a new aspirin product.

Answers

To Tests

CHAPTER 1 TEST, FORM A

1. c	2. d	3. b	4. c	5. a
6. a	7. d	8. c	9. c	10. a
11. 0	12. 0	13. 0	14. +	15. 0
16. +	17. +	18. 0	19. +	20. +

21. ordinary human or animal
22. norms
23. insights
24. mnemonic
25. shaping
26. dualism
27. Applied
28. 100-120
29. free association and/or dreams
30. Galton
31. Watson
32. reinforcement
33. applied
34. Educational
35. Experimental

36. f	37. j	38. h	39. c	40. e
41. b	42. i	43. g	44. d	45. a

46. Basic science refers to research designed to find out more about human behavior. Applied science refers to the practical applications of the principles discovered in basic science research. An example of the difference between these fields is studying the ability of infants to perceive visual patterns (basic science) and using the results of such a study to design a crib (applied science).

47. Some subspecializations found in contemporary psychology include counseling psychology (helping people deal with their personal problems), personality psychology (study personality development and traits), social psychology (study the way groups influence individual behavior), developmental psychology (study development as something that continues from birth to old age), educational psychology (study topics related to teaching children and young adults), community psychology (work in community mental health facilities, aid citizens' interactions with civil agencies), industrial psychology (study individuals in the workplace), and experimental psychology (investigate basic science problems).

CHAPTER 1 TEST, FORM B

1. d	2. b	3. c	4. b	5. a
6. d	7. d	8. a	9. d	10. c
11. +	12. 0	13. 0	14. +	15. 0
16. 0	17. +	18. 0	19. 0	20. +

21. behaviorists	22. legal
23. China	24. hypothesis
25. Basic	26. Physiological
27. Wundt	28. Copernicus
29. Freud	30. introspection
31. prediction	32. physical
33. cognitive	34. psychotherapists
35. Humanistic	

36. a	37. g	38. e	39. d	40. h
41. i	42. b	43. c	44. j	45. f

46. Historical trends found in modern psychology include the study of the human mind and thought processes, the study of the unconscious mind, studying the effect of heredity and environment on behavior, and the study of observable facts of behavior.

47. Some reasons for studying psychology include to gain insight into human behavior and learn useful procedures developed by psychologists that can be applied to everyday life.

CHAPTER 2 TEST, FORM A

1. d	2. c	3. b	4. c	5. d
6. a	7. b	8. b	9. c	10. a
11. 0	12. +	13. +	14. 0	15. +
16. 0	17. +	18. 0	19. +	20. 0

21. Learning
22. unconditioned
23. generalization
24. Watson
25. extinction
26. operant
27. reinforcements
28. four
29. fixed interval
30. conditioned or secondary
31. increases
32. positive
33. patterns
34. immediate or positive
35. token economy

36. b   **37.** a   **38.** j   **39.** f   **40.** d
41. c   **42.** e   **43.** h   **44.** g   **45.** i

46. Student responses will likely describe a design involving classical conditioning. The design should identify a conditioned stimulus that causes the conditioned response of fear of a rabbit. A plan to reverse this fear will most likely involve the principles of classical conditioning.

47. Factors that affect the learning process include feedback, transfer, reinforcement, punishment, transfer, and practice.

CHAPTER 2 TEST, FORM B

1. b   **2.** b   **3.** d   **4.** d   **5.** c
6. b   **7.** b   **8.** c   **9.** a   **10.** b
11. +   **12.** 0   **13.** +   **14.** +   **15.** +
16. 0   **17.** 0   **18.** +   **19.** 0   **20.** 0

21. classical   **22.** conditioned
23. stimulus   **24.** discrimination
25. aversion   **26.** continuous
27. ratio   **28.** repeated
29. negative   **30.** negative
31. helplessness   **32.** Escape
33. token economy   **34.** Transfer
35. modeling

36. i   **37.** j   **38.** h   **39.** e   **40.** g
41. d   **42.** b   **43.** a   **44.** f   **45.** c

46. Classical conditioning is a learning process in which a stimulus that normally elicits a given response is repeatedly preceded by a neutral stimulus. Eventually, the neutral stimulus will evoke a similar response when presented by itself. Operant conditioning is a form of conditioning in which a certain action is reinforced or punished, resulting in corresponding increases or decreases in the likelihood that similar actions will occur again.

47. Student responses should describe a plan that employs the principles of classical conditioning, operant conditioning, or modeling.

CHAPTER 3 TEST, FORM A

1. c   **2.** a   **3.** c   **4.** c   **5.** d
6. b   **7.** d   **8.** d   **9.** a   **10.** c
11. 0   **12.** +   **13.** +   **14.** 0   **15.** 0
16. +   **17.** +   **18.** +   **19.** +   **20.** +

21. information
22. selective attention
23. Feature extraction
24. Sensory storage
25. short-term
26. Long-term
27. SQ3R
28. recognize
29. Recall
30. Eidetic memory
31. Repression
32. symbols
33. Directed
34. strategies
35. Functional fixedness

36. i   **37.** d   **38.** h   **39.** f   **40.** g
41. e   **42.** b   **43.** j   **44.** c   **45.** a

46. Answers will vary, but some techniques used to improve memory include making the data meaningful, associating the data with things already stored in the memory, overlearning the data, and using mnemonic devices.

47. Answers will vary. Causes of forgetting include decay, interference, and repression.

CHAPTER 3 TEST, FORM B

1. b   **2.** b   **3.** b   **4.** c   **5.** d
6. d   **7.** a   **8.** b   **9.** d   **10.** c
11. 0   **12.** +   **13.** +   **14.** 0   **15.** +
16. +   **17.** 0   **18.** 0   **19.** 0   **20.** +

21. uncertainty   **22.** memorize
23. image   **24.** concept
25. seven   **26.** Semantic
27. thinking   **28.** set
29. Interference   **30.** Creativity
31. recombination   **32.** rule
33. Output   **34.** Input
35. insight

36. b   **37.** a   **38.** c   **39.** e   **40.** f
41. j   **42.** h   **43.** i   **44.** g   **45.** d

46. Creativity is the ability to use information in such a way that the result is somehow new, original, and meaningful. The parts of this process include flexibility and the ability to recombine elements to achieve insight.

47. Sensory storage holds information for only an instant. Short-term memory keeps information in mind for about 20 seconds. Long-term memory stores information indefinitely. Student examples will vary.

CHAPTER 4 TEST, FORM A

1. b	2. d	3. a	4. d	5. d
6. c	7. c	8. d	9. b	10. c
11. 0	12. 0	13. +	14. +	15. 0
16. +	17. 0	18. +	19. +	20. 0
21. 0	22. 0	23. +	24. 0	25. 0

26. effectors	27. parasympathetic
28. pons	29. corpus callosum
30. adrenalin	31. left
32. psychosurgery	33. sign stimulus
34. Monozygotic	35. PKU

36. d	37. c	38. j	39. g	40. i
41. a	42. b	43. e	44. f	45. h

46. The brain receives messages from receptors, cells whose function is to gather information. The brain sifts through these messages, combines them, and sends out orders to the effectors, cells that work the muscles, internal glands, and organs. Both types of messages travel along the nerves.

47. The study of animals can help in the study of human beings because human beings are believed to have evolved from more primitive animal origins, and their bodies are therefore similar to the bodies of other animals.

CHAPTER 4 TEST, FORM B

1. c	2. b	3. d	4. b	5. d
6. a	7. b	8. d	9. c	10. c
11. 0	12. +	13. 0	14. +	15. +
16. +	17. 0	18. 0	19. +	20. +
21. +	22. 0	23. 0	24. 0	25. 0

26. synapses
27. vertebrae
28. reticular activating system
29. association
30. corpus callosum
31. pituitary
32. instinct
33. Sociobiology
34. genetic
35. diet

36. j	37. i	38. d	39. c	40. e
41. h	42. f	43. a	44. b	45. g

46. It is difficult to resolve the nature-nurture problem because inherited factors and environmental conditions always act together in complicated ways.

47. Some methods used by psychologists to explore the brain are recording, stimulation, and lesioning.

CHAPTER 5 TEST, FORM A

1. c	2. d	3. b	4. d	5. b
6. d	7. c	8. a	9. c	10. c
11. +	12. +	13. +	14. +	15. +
16. 0	17. 0	18. 0	19. 0	20. 0
21. 0	22. 0	23. 0	24. 0	25. 0

26. perception	27. stimulus
28. low	29. absolute
30. retina	31. binocular fusion
32. decibels	33. four
34. Proximity	35. constancy

36. j	37. e	38. h	39. a	40. d
41. i	42. c	43. g	44. b	45. f

46. Weber's law is the principle that the larger or stronger a stimulus, the larger the change required for an observer to notice a difference. An example of this principle is adding a three-pound package into an empty backpack as compared to adding the same amount to a hundred-pound backpack.

47. In perceptual organization, the brain receives information from the senses and organizes and interprets it into meaningful experiences. Gestalt laws explain how bits and pieces of information are organized into meaningful objects and patterns. Through perceptual inference the individual fills in gaps in what the senses tell him or her. Through consistency, an experience is divided into the figure and the ground.

CHAPTER 5 TEST, FORM B

1. a	2. b	3. d	4. b	5. c
6. b	7. a	8. a	9. c	10. b
11. 0	12. +	13. +	14. 0	15. 0
16. 0	17. 0	18. +	19. 0	20. +
21. +	22. +	23. 0	24. 0	25. 0

26. difference	27. psychophysics
28. difference	29. Weber's law
30. more	31. auditory
32. Smell/taste	33. adapt
34. larger or stronger	35. illusions

36. j	37. b	38. h	39. f	40. a
41. d	42. i	43. c	44. e	45. g

46. Light enters the eye through the pupil. It reaches the lens, which focuses the light on the retina. Light-sensitive receptor cells on the retina, called rods and cones, change the light energy into chemical and electrical impulses. These impulses travel over the optic nerve to the brain.

47. The lowest level of physical energy that will produce a sensation in half the trials is the absolute threshold. The smallest change in a physical stimulus that produces a change in sensation in half the trials is the difference threshold.

CHAPTER 6 TEST, FORM A

1. b	2. c	3. a	4. a	5. b
6. d	7. b	8. a	9. d	10. a
11. c	12. c	13. d	14. 0	15. 0
16. +	17. 0	18. +	19. +	20. +
21. 0	22. 0	23. +	24. +	25. +

26. goal directed	27. lateral
28. more	29. external
30. Hull	31. social
32. artistically	33. emotions
34. learning	35. thalamus

36. a	37. c	38. i	39. d	40. b
41. g	42. e	43. h	44. f	45. j

46. Maslow placed achievement motivation in the context of a hierarchy of needs all people share. According to Maslow's scheme, people need to first satisfy their fundamental needs, then their psychological needs, and finally their self-actualization needs.

47. Motivation generally refers to the needs, desires, and mental calculations that lead to goal-directed behavior. Emotions generally refer to the feelings associated with such decisions and activities.

CHAPTER 6 TEST, FORM B

1. c	2. b	3. c	4. c	5. d
6. b	7. d	8. b	9. a	10. b
11. b	12. a	13. a	14. 0	15. 0
16. +	17. 0	18. +	19. 0	20. 0
21. 0	22. 0	23. +	24. 0	25. +

26. homeostasis	27. ventromedial
28. Drive reduction	29. habit
30. less	31. TAT
32. psychological	33. innate
34. James-Lange	35. Cognitive

36. b	37. e	38. a	39. d	40. j
41. f	42. h	43. c	44. i	45. g

46. Physiological theories of emotion associate feelings with sudden increases or decreases in energy, muscle tension, relaxation, and sensations in the pit of the stomach. Cognitive theories of emotion are based on the idea that bodily changes and thinking work together to produce emotions.

47. The drive-reduction theory was abandoned because it overlooked the fact that certain experiences such as hugging are inherently pleasurable and as such can serve as incentives or goals for behavior. Another factor overlooked was that humans and related animals derive pleasure from stimulation or arousal.

CHAPTER 7 TEST, FORM A

1. d	2. a	3. d	4. b	5. d
6. a	7. a	8. d	9. a	10. c
11. d	12. c	13. c	14. c	15. a
16. d	17. d	18. d	19. 0	20. +
21. +	22. +	23. +	24. 0	25. +
26. 0	27. 0	28. +	29. +	30. 0

31. consciousness	32. EEG
33. IV	34. commonplace
35. hallucinate	

36. c	37. e	38. d	39. f	40. h
41. j	42. a	43. b	44. g	45. i

46. Hallucinations are sensations or perceptions that have no direct external cause or feeling things that do not exist. People may hallucinate due to hypnosis, meditation, drug use or withdrawal, and psychological breakdown. Other situations that can result in a hallucination include when dreaming, when deprived of sleep, and during periods of high emotion, concentration, or fatigue.

47. The relaxation response is said to be physiologically distinct from more casual states of relaxation or sleep. Four basic elements are needed to elicit this response: a quiet environment, a comfortable position, a mental device, and a passive attitude.

CHAPTER 7 TEST, FORM B

1. d	2. c	3. b	4. d	5. b
6. b	7. a	8. d	9. c	10. +
11. +	12. 0	13. 0	14. +	15. 0
16. 0	17. 0	18. 0	19. +	20. +
21. 0	22. 0	23. +	24. 0	25. 0
26. 0	27. +	28. +	29. +	30. +

31. sleep	32. III
33. REM	34. symbolism
35. central	

36. h	37. c	38. i	39. a	40. j
41. b	42. e	43. d	44. g	45. f

46. Biofeedback involves learning to control your internal physiological processes with the help of feedback from these physiological states. Biofeedback has been used to treat such physical ailments as migraine headaches, partial paralysis, and epilepsy.

47. According to the neo-dissociation theory, consciousness includes many different aspects that may become separated, or dissociated, during hypnosis. As a result, people who are hypnotized are very suggestible and can more easily imagine and remember things. Some psychologists, such as Theodore Barber, feel that hypnosis is not a special state of consciousness. Another explanation of hypnosis is based on the importance of suggestibility in the hypnotic induction. According to some theorists, hypnotized people behave as they do because they have accepted the role of a hypnotized subject.

CHAPTER 8 TEST, FORM A

1. b	**2.** c	**3.** c	**4.** b	**5.** c
6. a	**7.** b	**8.** b	**9.** d	**10.** b
11. a	**12.** d	**13.** b	**14.** 0	**15.** 0
16. +	**17.** +	**18.** +	**19.** 0	**20.** 0
21. +	**22.** +	**23.** 0	**24.** 0	**25.** 0
26. 0	**27.** 0	**28.** 0		

29. rooting	**30.** manner
31. formal operations	**32.** telegraphic
33. identifying	**34.** Erikson
35. cognitive	

36. c	**37.** j	**38.** i	**39.** a	**40.** b
41. g	**42.** h	**43.** d	**44.** e	**45.** f

46. Social learning theorists believe the development of morality is the result of conditioning and imitation. Cognitive theorists believe there are six stages of moral development, and that in order to reach the highest levels of development, the individual must be able to see other people's points of view.

47. As a result of animal research, some psychologists feel that there is a critical period during which infants need to become attached to a mothering person. In addition, some psychologists feel that children who are temporarily or permanently separated from their mothers develop abnormally. However, new research suggests that inadequate care and lack of learning opportunities, not mother deprivation, cause these problems.

CHAPTER 8 TEST, FORM B

1. c	**2.** b	**3.** c	**4.** b	**5.** d
6. c	**7.** d	**8.** d	**9.** b	**10.** d
11. d	**12.** a	**13.** c	**14.** 0	**15.** +
16. +	**17.** 0	**18.** 0	**19.** +	**20.** +
21. 0	**22.** 0	**23.** +	**24.** 0	**25.** +
26. +	**27.** +	**28.** +		

29. Piaget
30. object permanence
31. grammar
32. socialization
33. latency
34. autonomy/doubt
35. egocentric

36. d	**37.** c	**38.** g	**39.** i	**40.** e
41. b	**42.** a	**43.** j	**44.** f	**45.** h

46. According to Piaget, cognitive development occurs in the following four stages: sensorimotor state (when thinking is displayed in actions), preoperation stage (which marks the beginning of symbolic representation), concrete operation stage (marked by the ability to understand conservation problems), and formal operational stage (when thinking becomes more abstract and hypothetical).

47. The newborn is capable of certain coordinated movement patterns or reflexes that are triggered by a particular stimulus. The grasping reflex is a response to a touch on the palm of the hand. The rooting reflex refers to a newborn's response to a touch on the cheek by opening his or her mouth and turning his or her head.

CHAPTER 9 TEST, FORM A

1. c	**2.** c	**3.** d	**4.** c	**5.** d
6. a	**7.** b	**8.** a	**9.** c	**10.** c
11. +	**12.** +	**13.** 0	**14.** +	**15.** +
16. 0	**17.** +	**18.** +	**19.** 0	**20.** 0
21. 0	**22.** +	**23.** 0	**24.** 0	**25.** 0

26. laissez-faire	**27.** Erikson
28. Hall	**29.** Puberty
30. authoritative	**31.** clique
32. six	**33.** Rationalization
34. androgynous	**35.** democratic

36. g	**37.** b	**38.** d	**39.** f	**40.** h
41. e	**42.** a	**43.** i	**44.** j	**45.** c

46. Student responses may include the following conflicts: acquiring a masculine or feminine sex role, developing appropriate relations with agemates, becoming emotionally

independent, deciding on a vocation, achieving socially responsible behavior, and acquiring values that are harmonious with an appropriate scientific world picture.

47. Responses supporting Bem's androgynous roles will likely describe such roles as flexible, allowing an individual to define himself according to his talents, temperament, and values. Responses against such roles will likely explain that not all members of society are accepting of such roles.

CHAPTER 9 TEST, FORM B

1. c	**2.** b	**3.** c	**4.** d	**5.** d
6. d	**7.** d	**8.** b	**9.** d	**10.** b
11. 0	**12.** +	**13.** +	**14.** +	**15.** +
16. +	**17.** 0	**18.** 0	**19.** +	**20.** 0
21. 0	**22.** 0	**23.** +	**24.** 0	**25.** +

26. Puberty	**27.** social learning
28. transition	**29.** Samoa
30. authoritarian	**31.** conformity
32. adolescent	**33.** identity
34. Initiation	**35.** Mead

36. h	**37.** i	**38.** d	**39.** j	**40.** f
41. a	**42.** e	**43.** b	**44.** c	**45.** g

46. During adolescence, the individual struggles to arrive at an integrated sense of self or identity. According to Erikson, this occurs through a time of storm and stress called an identity crisis. Other psychologists argue that this period is not necessarily marked by crisis.

47. During adolescence, the thinking patterns characteristic of adults emerge. Thinking becomes more abstract and less concrete. The individual is able to understand abstract principles. These new intellectual capacities enable the adolescent to deal with overpowering emotional feelings through rationalization.

CHAPTER 10 TEST, FORM A

1. c	**2.** c	**3.** c	**4.** d	**5.** b
6. c	**7.** c	**8.** b	**9.** a	**10.** a
11. +	**12.** +	**13.** +	**14.** +	**15.** 0
16. +	**17.** +	**18.** +	**19.** +	**20.** 0
21. +	**22.** 0	**23.** +	**24.** 0	**25.** 0

26. Freud	**27.** reaction time
28. men	**29.** stagnation
30. 80	**31.** acceptance

32. hospice		**33.** closed		
34. Wechsler		**35.** ageism		

36. c	**37.** j	**38.** d	**39.** f	**40.** i
41. e	**42.** g	**43.** b	**44.** h	**45.** a

46. Levinson's model of adult male development is broken down into three major areas. The period from about age 17 to age 40 is called the early adult era. Middle adult era encompasses age 40 to 60, while the late adult era begins at about age 60. In between these eras are important transition periods at ages 30, 40, 50, and 60, which last approximately five years. Student examples of these stages will vary.

47. Societal attitudes toward aging are often based on the decremental model of aging. This holds that progressive physical and mental decline is inevitable with age. Such thinking results in the false notions that elderly are unproductive, senile, and inflexible. The effect of these attitudes, in addition to changes in the life situation of an elderly person, have a negative impact on the person's self-image.

CHAPTER 10 TEST, FORM B

1. a	**2.** d	**3.** b	**4.** a	**5.** a
6. d	**7.** b	**8.** b	**9.** d	**10.** a
11. 0	**12.** +	**13.** +	**14.** +	**15.** 0
16. +	**17.** 0	**18.** +	**19.** 0	**20.** 0
21. +	**22.** 0	**23.** 0	**24.** +	**25.** +

26. menopause	**27.** generativity
28. 40	**29.** decremental
30. 30	**31.** Thanatology
32. less	**33.** open
34. five	**35.** Fluid

36. i	**37.** a	**38.** c	**39.** g	**40.** b
41. d	**42.** h	**43.** e	**44.** f	**45.** j

46. Kübler-Ross's stages of psychological adjustment to terminal illness are denial, anger, bargaining, depression, and, finally, acceptance.

47. During the aging process, physical strength and the five senses decline. However, the majority of the elderly are able to carry out their normal activities. The elderly are subject to disease just as young people are. For the most part, the health of an older person is related to his or her health when younger. The majority of people over the age of 65 continue to be interested in sex, and healthy partners enjoy sexual activities into their 70s and 80s.

CHAPTER 11 TEST, FORM A

1. b	2. a	3. d	4. c	5. b
6. d	7. d	8. d	9. c	10. b
11. c	12. a	13. c	14. b	15. d
16. +	17. +	18. 0	19. 0	20. +

21. Freud
22. id
23. ego
24. superego
25. displacement
26. repression
27. reaction formation
28. projection
29. regression
30. collective unconscious
31. archetypes
32. inferiority
33. organism
34. idiographic
35. Rogers

36. h	37. f	38. a	39. e	40. g
41. b	42. i	43. j	44. d	45. c

46. Defense mechanisms are certain specific means by which the ego unconsciously protects itself against unpleasant impulses or circumstances. Displacement, repression, reaction formation, projection, and regression are all types of defense mechanisms.

47. Freud was the first modern psychologist to suggest that every personality has a large unconscious component. He believed that unconscious motives and the feelings people experience as children have an enormous impact on adult personality and behavior. Skinner and other behaviorists do not focus attention on unconscious processes. Rather, they only study observable behavior. Carl Rogers's theories emphasizes personal experience rather than drives and instincts. he believed that many people suffer from a conflict between what they value in themselves and what they learn other people value in them. Trait theories also disregard unconscious processes. Trait theorists believe a few basic traits are central for all people and that a particular trait causes a person to respond in a certain way to different situations.

CHAPTER 11 TEST, FORM B

1. d	2. b	3. c	4. d	5. d
6. a	7. b	8. c	9. d	10. c
11. +	12. +	13. +	14. +	15. 0

16. 0	17. 0	18. +	19. +	20. +
21. 0	22. +	23. +	24. +	25. 0

26. Adler
27. behaviorist
28. contingencies
29. observational
30. social environment
31. Kelly
32. learning
33. self-actualization
34. Maslow
35. fully-functioning

36. f	37. d	38. c	39. i	40. e
41. j	42. g	43. b	44. h	45. a

46. The behavioral model of personality holds that as individuals differ in their learning experiences, they acquire different behaviors and hence different personalities. The humanistic model of personality is founded on the belief that all human beings strive for self-actualization.

47. Students will likely categorize the theories of Freud as pessimistic, while those of Jung, Adler, Skinner, Maslow, and Rogers are optimistic.

CHAPTER 12 TEST, FORM A

1. d	2. c	3. b	4. d	5. a
6. d	7. c	8. a	9. a	10. d
11. 0	12. 0	13. +	14. +	15. 0
16. 0	17. 0	18. 0	19. 0	20. +
21. +	22. +	23. 0	24. 0	25. 0

26. reliability
27. percentile
28. mental/chronological
29. adults
30. SAT (or GATB)
31. Strong Vocational Interest Inventory
32. Minnesota Multiphasic Personality Inventory
33. Rorschach ink-blot test
34. situational
35. interest

36. j	37. g	38. f	39. d	40. c
41. e	42. h	43. i	44. b	45. a

46. Reliability is the ability of a test to give the same results under a variety of different circumstances. Validity is the ability of a test to measure what it is intended to measure. Norms are standards of comparison for test results developed by giving the test to large, well-defined groups of people.

47. Ways of reducing test-taking anxiety include adequate preparation for the test, getting enough sleep the night before the text, allowing plenty of time to get to the testing site, managing the time you have to complete the test, having a strategy for taking the test, and believing in yourself.

47. Short-term psychological reactions to stress include anxiety, anger, fear, difficulty in concentrating or thinking, and unjustified suspicion of others. Long-term psychological reactions to stress affects mental health and increases the likelihood of psychiatric disorder.

CHAPTER TEST 12, FORM B

1. b	**2.** a	**3.** d	**4.** a	**5.** d
6. b	**7.** b	**8.** c	**9.** c	**10.** c
11. +	**12.** 0	**13.** +	**14.** +	**15.** +
16. +	**17.** 0	**18.** +	**19.** 0	**20.** +
21. 0	**22.** +	**23.** 0	**24.** 0	**25.** +

26. raw
27. norming
28. standardized
29. 100
30. projective
31. SAT (or GATB)
32. Validity
33. Alpha
34. Beta
35. family size

36. e	**37.** f	**38.** a	**39.** c	**40.** g
41. j	**42.** d	**43.** i	**44.** h	**45.** b

46. Freud proposes that many emotions, feelings, and thoughts are found in the unconscious. Personality consists of three parts: the id, the ego, and the superego.

47. One of its premises is the basic goodness of people. It considers as the core of personality a person's ability to change and to improve.

CHAPTER TEST 13, FORM A

1. c	**2.** d	**3.** a	**4.** a	**5.** c
6. b	**7.** a	**8.** a	**9.** c	**10.** a
11. +	**12.** 0	**13.** 0	**14.** +	**15.** +
16. 0	**17.** 0	**18.** 0	**19.** +	**20.** 0
21. +	**22.** +	**23.** 0	**24.** +	**25.** +

26. eustress
27. distress
28. 3
29. A
30. alarm
31. 70
32. double approach-avoidance
33. work
34. optimist
35. pessimist

36. i	**37.** b	**38.** d	**39.** j	**40.** a
41. e	**42.** h	**43.** g	**44.** f	**45.** c

46. Holmes and Rahe found that as the nature of a stressful event increased the likelihood of the individual to become ill also increased.

CHAPTER TEST 13, FORM B

1. a	**2.** b	**3.** d	**4.** c	**5.** d
6. c	**7.** d	**8.** c	**9.** b	**10.** b
11. 0	**12.** 0	**13.** +	**14.** 0	**15.** 0
16. 0	**17.** 0	**18.** +	**19.** 0	**20.** +
21. 0	**22.** 0	**23.** +	**24.** 0	**25.** 0

26. three
27. fight or flight
28. stress
29. Adrenalin
30. death of a spouse
31. denial
32. approach-avoidance
33. frustration
34. holistic
35. cognitive

36. i	**37.** j	**38.** c	**39.** b	**40.** h
41. f	**42.** e	**43.** d	**44.** a	**45.** g

46. Psychological stress-coping strategies include denial, intellectualization, and cognitive preparation. Behavioral stress-coping strategies include controlling stressful situations, confronting the matter head-on, physical exercise, and support groups.

47. Stress is considered a major cause of illness today, and one study shows that up to 80 percent of all disease may relate back to stress as its cause. Stress can cause disease directly or indirectly. Student examples will vary, and should mention the Holmes-Rahe study.

CHAPTER TEST 14, FORM A

1. b	**2.** b	**3.** c	**4.** c	**5.** d
6. c	**7.** b	**8.** c	**9.** d	**10.** b
11. +	**12.** +	**13.** 0	**14.** 0	**15.** +
16. 0	**17.** 0	**18.** 0	**19.** +	**20.** +
21. 0	**22.** 0	**23.** +	**24.** 0	**25.** +

26. shaping
27. Love
28. commitment
29. need
30. divorce
31. adolescents
32. generation gap
33. Permissive
34. autonomy
35. resources

36. h   **37.** f   **38.** c   **39.** b   **40.** g
41. d   **42.** a   **43.** i   **44.** e   **45.** j

46. Rubin found that liking is based primarily on respect for another person and the feeling that he or she is similar to you. Rubin identified three major components of romantic love: need, the desire to give, and intimacy.

47. College life stimulates change in that the new environment may challenge the identity a student established in high school. College also exposes the individual to a great diversity in religious and ethnic backgrounds, family income levels, and attitudes. A positive way of coping with such change is by resynthesis or keeping one's options open until they have enough information and experience to make a choice.

CHAPTER TEST 14, FORM B

1. a   **2.** c   **3.** d   **4.** b   **5.** c
6. b   **7.** d   **8.** b   **9.** b   **10.** c
11. 0   **12.** +   **13.** 0   **14.** 0   **15.** +
16. 0   **17.** 0   **18.** 0   **19.** +   **20.** 0
21. +   **22.** +   **23.** 0   **24.** 0   **25.** +

26. companionate
27. caring, or the desire to give
28. social group
29. attributes
30. Separation
31. children
32. psychoanalyzing
33. judging or criticizing
34. name-calling or shaming
35. Liking

36. b   **37.** g   **38.** j   **39.** c   **40.** a
41. e   **42.** i   **43.** f   **44.** d   **45.** h

46. Healthy adjustment to marriage depends on several factors, including: whether the couple's needs are compatible; whether their images of themselves coincide with their images of each other; whether they agree on what their individual roles should be within the marriage.

47. Most divorced people go through a period of mourning and separation shock. Emotions such as anger, fear, loneliness, anxiety, and failure generally surface. Children involved in a divorce must deal with a conflict that they do not understand and have no control over. Divorce is especially difficult on young children who do not possess the emotional maturity to deal with the situation. Fortunately, both parents and their children do eventually come to terms with divorce.

CHAPTER TEST 15, FORM A

1. a   **2.** c   **3.** b   **4.** c   **5.** b
6. c   **7.** c   **8.** b   **9.** a   **10.** d
11. 0   **12.** 0   **13.** +   **14.** +   **15.** +
16. +   **17.** 0   **18.** +   **19.** +   **20.** 0
21. +   **22.** 0   **23.** 0   **24.** +   **25.** 0

26. deviance
27. adjust
28. phobia
29. compulsion
30. somatoform disorder
31. dissociative
32. Schizophrenia
33. catatonic type
34. Double blind
35. alcoholism

36. i   **37.** j   **38.** b   **39.** h   **40.** g
41. a   **42.** d   **43.** e   **44.** c   **45.** f

46. Responses will likely argue that mental illness is a severe psychological problem that disrupts the individual's everyday life. Responses should also explain that professionals need to be very cautious when judging a person to be mentally ill just because he or she acts in a way not easily understood.

47. Answers will vary. No single definition is totally adequate, but perhaps the best working definition of abnormal behavior is one based on the psychological consequences of the behavior, which are thought of as abnormal if they produce distress, anxiety, guilt, or if they are harmful to others.

CHAPTER TEST 15, FORM B

1. b   **2.** d   **3.** d   **4.** d   **5.** b
6. b   **7.** a   **8.** a   **9.** c   **10.** c
11. +   **12.** +   **13.** +   **14.** 0   **15.** +
16. 0   **17.** 0   **18.** 0   **19.** +   **20.** 0
21. +   **22.** +   **23.** +   **24.** 0   **25.** +

26. addiction
27. flashbacks
28. amnesia
29. conversion disorder
30. fugue
31. obsession
32. delusions
33. predisposition
34. antisocial
35. axes

36. d   **37.** g   **38.** f   **39.** i   **40.** a
41. c   **42.** j   **43.** b   **44.** h   **45.** e

46. People have a psychoactive substance use disorder when they have trouble refraining from the use of a psychoactive drug, even though that drug is causing serious social, occupational, or medical problems.

47. Both anxiety disorders are characterized by emotional distress due to feelings of apprehension, inadequacy, or fear. In panic disorder a person suffers sudden, inexplicable attacks of intense fear. People suffering from phobic disorder experience an inappropriate, exaggerated fear of an object or situation.

CHAPTER 16 TEST, FORM A

1. b	**2.** c	**3.** c	**4.** c	**5.** a
6. c	**7.** d	**8.** d	**9.** b	**10.** c
11. +	**12.** +	**13.** 0	**14.** +	**15.** 0
16. 0	**17.** +	**18.** +	**19.** 0	**20.** +
21. 0	**22.** +	**23.** 0	**24.** +	**25.** +

26. symptom	**27.** Psychoanalysts
28. frustration	**29.** insight
30. resistance	**31.** Rogers's
32. Gestalt	**33.** behavior
34. commitment	**35.** systematic desensitization

36. f	**37.** h	**38.** i	**39.** e	**40.** g
41. d	**42.** c	**43.** j	**44.** a	**45.** b

46. Psychotherapy is a general term for treatment used by social workers, psychologists, and psychiatrists to help troubled individuals overcome their problems. The goal of psychotherapy is to break the behavior patterns that lead to unhappiness and strengthen the individual's control over his or her life.

47. Behavior therapists seek to change undesirable behavior through conditioning techniques. Psychoanalysts make their patients aware of their unconscious motives so that they can gain control over their behavior and free themselves of self-defeating patterns.

CHAPTER 16 TEST, FORM B

1. b	**2.** a	**3.** a	**4.** d	**5.** c
6. c	**7.** a	**8.** c	**9.** c	**10.** a
11. +	**12.** 0	**13.** 0	**14.** +	**15.** +
16. 0	**17.** 0	**18.** +	**19.** 0	**20.** 0
21. +	**22.** 0	**23.** 0	**24.** 0	**25.** +

26. placebo	**27.** Psychiatrists
28. Freud	**29.** free association
30. humanistic	**31.** Frankl

32. rational-emotive **33.** Paraprofessionals
34. Crisis intervention **35.** transference

36. h	**37.** g	**38.** e	**39.** j	**40.** c
41. i	**42.** b	**43.** d	**44.** a	**45.** f

46. Eysenck's research concluded that psychotherapy was no more effective than no treatment at all. Bergin said rate of improvement for untreated patients was much lower than Eysenck claimed. Smith and Glass found that psychotherapy is generally more effective than no treatment, and that on the average most forms of therapy have similar effects.

47. Behavior therapy is a form of therapy aimed at changing undesirable behavior through conditioning techniques. Rational-emotive therapy is a form of therapy aimed at changing unrealistic assumptions about oneself and other people. It is believed that once a person understands that he or she has been acting on false beliefs, self-defeating thoughts and behaviors will be avoided. Transactional analysis is a form of therapy aimed at helping clients become more flexible by discovering maladaptive strategies for living that they acquired while growing up and which restrict them as adults.

CHAPTER 17 TEST, FORM A

1. a	**2.** d	**3.** c	**4.** b	**5.** d
6. c	**7.** b	**8.** c	**9.** c	**10.** d
11. 0	**12.** +	**13.** 0	**14.** 0	**15.** +
16. 0	**17.** 0	**18.** +	**19.** +	**20.** 0
21. +	**22.** 0	**23.** 0	**24.** +	**25.** +

26. Social	**27.** uncertainties
28. ego-support	**29.** stimulation
30. roles	**31.** nine
32. Attribution theory	**33.** stereotypes
34. task	**35.** diffusion of responsibility

36. i	**37.** j	**38.** h	**39.** f	**40.** d
41. e	**42.** b	**43.** g	**44.** c	**45.** a

46. Responses will likely identify diffusion of responsibility and the tendency to minimize the need for response as reasons why a person would not help another in distress.

47. Variables that affect perception of another person include your own set of assumptions about how people behave and what traits or characteristics go together, stereotypes, and whether you attribute the person's actions to personal qualities or to a situation or role.

CHAPTER 17 TEST, FORM B

1. b	**2.** c	**3.** b	**4.** c	**5.** d
6. b	**7.** b	**8.** b	**9.** d	**10.** a
11. 0	**12.** 0	**13.** 0	**14.** 0	**15.** 0
16. +	**17.** +	**18.** 0	**19.** +	**20.** +
21. 0	**22.** 0	**23.** +	**24.** 0	**25.** 0

26. companionship **27.** utility
28. assumptions **29.** complementary
30. 10 **31.** Hall
32. sociogram **33.** output
34. group **35.** similar

36. j	**37.** b	**38.** i	**39.** c	**40.** e
41. g	**42.** f	**43.** d	**44.** h	**45.** a

46. Personal space refers to an area of privacy most people surround themselves with. If this bubble of privacy is invaded by another individual, one generally feels slightly threatened, imposed upon, and uncomfortable. However, intimates are usually welcomed into the bubble. Examples of this social behavior may include positions at a beach, distance between a speaker's podium and the audience, and locations in a crowded elevator.

47. Responses will likely identify diffusion of responsibility and the tendency to minimize the need for response as reasons why a person would not help another in distress.

CHAPTER 18 TEST, FORM A

1. a	**2.** d	**3.** d	**4.** c	**5.** b
6. a	**7.** b	**8.** c	**9.** c	**10.** c
11. +	**12.** 0	**13.** +	**14.** +	**15.** +
16. +	**17.** 0	**18.** 0	**19.** +	**20.** +
21. +	**22.** +	**23.** +	**24.** 0	**25.** +

26. compliance
27. internalization
28. attitudes
29. self-fulfilling prophecy
30. discrimination
31. dissonance
32. sleeper
33. Milgram
34. boomerang
35. cooperate

36. g	**37.** i	**38.** b	**39.** h	**40.** c
41. a	**42.** e	**43.** h	**44.** d	**45.** f

46. The best way to get an idea across to another is to make sure the idea or message is only one part, be sure that the source of the message is respected and admired, present the message through personal contact, and be sure that the appropriate audience receives the message.

47. Attitudes are learned predispositions to react in a positive or negative manner to a particular object. People acquire attitudes through a number of ways, including classical and operant conditioning. Answers will vary, but students might note that, if two simultaneously held attitudes conflict with or contradict one another, people might resolve the dilemma by changing the attitude, changing the relative importance of one of the attitudes, denying that conflict exists.

CHAPTER 18 TEST, FORM B

1. b	**2.** c	**3.** b	**4.** d	**5.** b
6. d	**7.** c	**8.** b	**9.** d	**10.** b
11. 0	**12.** +	**13.** +	**14.** 0	**15.** 0
16. +	**17.** +	**18.** +	**19.** 0	**20.** 0
21. 0	**22.** +	**23.** 0	**24.** 0	**25.** 0

26. source **27.** scapegoat
28. Self-justification **29.** audience
30. channel **31.** message
32. brainwashing **33.** Central
34. Peripheral **35.** Prejudice

36. a	**37.** f	**38.** d	**39.** i	**40.** j
41. g	**42.** h	**43.** c	**44.** b	**45.** e

46. Research suggests that cognitive dissonance can cause changes in socially important values. An example of this phenomena is the experiment in which students were made aware that their emphasis on freedom was inconsistent with their indifference to equality and civil rights.

47. Milgram's research showed that people assume that an authority knows what it is doing, even when the instructions seem to run counter to common standards of moral behavior. It also showed that social conditioning for obeying legitimate authorities is so strongly ingrained that people often lack the means to oppose the authority. These findings could explain the acquiescence of the German nation to Hitlerism.

CHAPTER 19 TEST, FORM A

1. a	**2.** c	**3.** d	**4.** b	**5.** d
6. c	**7.** b	**8.** a	**9.** b	**10.** d
11. +	**12.** +	**13.** 0	**14.** +	**15.** 0
16. 0	**17.** 0	**18.** +	**19.** 0	**20.** +
21. +	**22.** 0	**23.** 0	**24.** +	**25.** +

26. "Sesame Street"
27. men; women
28. APA, APS, CPA
29. importance (to system functioning)
30. visualization
31. abstract thinking (skills)
32. clinical
33. National Association for Mental Health
34. behavior
35. Dorothea Dix

| 36. e | 37. j | 38. i | 39. g | 40. f |
| 41. d | 42. a | 43. b | 44. h | 45. c |

46. Toffler's basic point is that the economies of the world are currently based on an assumption of unlimited natural resources that can be consumed and then thrown away and replaced. He argues that we should instead stress preserving our natural resources by the servicing of current appliances so as to extend their useful life.

47. Answers will vary, but should be drawn from the information contained in Table 19.2. Credit should be given for any logical extension from this table to other jobs and education correctly described.

CHAPTER 19 TEST, FORM B

1. b	2. c	3. c	4. d	5. c
6. a	7. a	8. a	9. c	10. b
11. +	12. 0	13. +	14. +	15. 0
16. +	17. 0	18. +	19. +	20. 0
21. +	22. 0	23. +	24. 0	25. 0

26. sports	27. Clifford Beers
28. SAT	29. applied
30. forensic	31. pituitary
32. B. F. Skinner	33. resources
34. 45	35. Head Start

| 36. c | 37. d | 38. e | 39. f | 40. i |
| 41. j | 42. b | 43. a | 44. g | 45. h |

46. Psychologists work in a variety of settings. Primary sites include universities, colleges, hospitals, clinics, community mental health centers, and counseling centers. Others have independent practices.

47. Answers will vary, but might include: the changing nature of the world population, in terms of growth, a growing elderly population, and an increase in average age; the growth of new technology.

CHAPTER 20 TEST, FORM A

1. c	2. b	3. b	4. a	5. d
6. c	7. d	8. c	9. a	10. b
11. +	12. +	13. 0	14. 0	15. +
16. 0	17. 0	18. 0	19. 0	20. +
21. 0	22. +	23. 0	24. +	25. 0

26. hypothesis
27. statistically significant
28. random
29. central tendency
30. predictions
31. range
32. control
33. case
34. control group
35. inferential statistics

| 36. j | 37. i | 38. e | 39. a | 40. h |
| 41. g | 42. c | 43. d | 44. f | 45. b |

46. Experiments will vary. However, all answers should indentify a hypothesis, independent variable, dependent variable, control group, and experimental group.

47. Researchers are interested in the statistical significance of the results of their research to determine whether the results are extreme enough so that they are more likely due to the variable being studied rather than chance.

CHAPTER 20 TEST, FORM B

1. b	2. c	3. c	4. c	5. b
6. b	7. b	8. d	9. c	10. b
11. +	12. +	13. 0	14. 0	15. +
16. +	17. 0	18. +	19. 0	20. +
21. 0	22. +	23. +	24. 0	25. 0

26. sample
27. statistics
28. sample
29. central tendency
30. average
31. positive
32. longitudinal
33. chance
34. naturalistic observation
35. decreases

| 36. a | 37. b | 38. c | 39. d | 40. e |
| 41. g | 42. f | 43. h | 44. j | 45. i |

46. Answers will vary. Students may note such factors as size of city (may not be a large population) and the idea that the city may be atypical.

47. Answers will vary. Students should show an understanding of the steps of the scientific methods.